Communication Experiments

Communication Experiments:
A Manual for Conducting Experiments

R. Wayne Pace
University of New Mexico

Brent D. Peterson
Brigham Young University

Robert R. Boren
Boise State University

Wadsworth Publishing Company, Inc.
Belmont, California

Designer: Ann Wilkinson

ISBN 0-534-00413-X

L. C. Cat. Card No. 74-33575

Printed in the United States of America

1 2 3 4 5 6 7 8 9 10 — 79 78 77 76 75

Preface

The primary objective of *Communication Experiments* is to encourage students to learn about communicative behavior by engaging in scientific research. Secondarily, by conducting experiments, students may learn by doing and thus discover for themselves the strengths and weaknesses of the information dealing with the communication process.

The order of the experiments follows the organization of the accompanying text, *Communication Behavior.* Each of the experiments described here has been adapted from actual research reported in a thesis, dissertation, or scholarly journal, and the source of the original report is cited at the beginning of each experiment. Although our adaptation is usually far simpler than the scholarly report, it may be beneficial from time to time to locate the original, read through the procedures and results, and compare what you do with what is described there. Occasionally, you may want to modify the procedures we have adopted to correspond more closely with the original. Just looking at the differences may be interesting.

Experiments about certain aspects of communication behavior are some of the most fascinating in the scientific world. As the sources of original reports reveal, scholars calling themselves communicologists, psychologists, sociologists, social psychologists, information scientists, and many other designations all study communication behavior. *Communication Experiments* contains studies that cover the wide range of scientific inquiry into the factors and situations we call communication.

The experiments in this manual were tested, using college students as subjects and with modifications suggested to make them easier to conduct in a classroom setting. Clarence E. Tapie Rohm, a graduate student at Brigham Young University, completed the test runs and aided considerably in clarifying procedures.

We are grateful to our students and colleagues who have contributed so much to the creation of this work through their research and publications. Wadsworth Publishing Company and Rebecca Hayden have been patient and persistent, traits of ever-consuming importance in the preparation of a book. Gae, Arlene, and Marj, our companions and helpmeets, continue as ever to inspire us beyond our fondest imaginings. May Polivka, Mary Ann Kline, and Anette Bradford have survived yet another publication bout and made form emerge from their typewriters where only shades and sketches once appeared.

RWP BDP RRB

Contents

Introduction: On Research   **1**

Part 1
Experiments about Relationships

Chapter 1
Interpersonal Dynamics   **15**
Experiment 1.1 Expressions of Warmth   15
Experiment 1.2 Interpersonal Hostility   23

Chapter 2
Improving Relationships   **31**
Experiment 2.1 Self-Disclosure and Trust   31
Experiment 2.2 Relevant Responses   45

Part 2
Experiments about Messages

Chapter 3
Message Reception and Processing   **67**
Experiment 3.1 Selective Perception   67
Experiment 3.2 Organization and Retention   73

Chapter 4
Message Preparation and Presentation   **85**
Experiment 4.1 Presenting Evidence   85
Experiment 4.2 Fear-Arousing Appeals   107

Part 3
Experiments about Information Diffusion

Chapter 5
Face-to-Face Groups   127
Experiment 5.1   Oral Lecture vs. Manuscript   127
Experiment 5.2   Seeing vs. Hearing a Speaker   139

Chapter 6
Social Groups   151
Experiment 6.1   Acquaintance Networks   151
Experiment 6.2   Communication Patterns in Small Groups   161

Chapter 7
Serial Groups   171
Experiment 7.1   Serial Reproduction of Information   171
Experiment 7.2   Reducing Error in Serial Communication   189

Part 4
Experiments about Achieving Change

Chapter 8
Individual Factors   197
Experiment 8.1   Credibility   197
Experiment 8.2   Attractiveness and Desire to Influence   209

Chapter 9
Small Group Factors   223
Experiment 9.1   Individual vs. Group Judgment   223
Experiment 9.2   Conformity   241

Chapter 10
Social Action Factors   257
Experiment 10.1   Two-Step Flow in Marketing   257
Experiment 10.2   Opinion Change and the Two-Step Flow   267

Conclusion: Beyond Research   279

Introduction:
On Research

As a field of study matures, it seeks to do more than talk about the old days and the old ways. Eventually, at least for those with professional concerns about the area, there is a desire to develop a discipline. A *discipline* is a branch of study or instruction with a body of knowledge based on scientific discoveries. A discipline has a set of *theories* that help to explain and unify the knowledge and information. Theories help scientists understand and predict what will happen in their fields.

In the discipline of communicology—the scientific study of communication—scientists attempt to develop theories that will explain how and why people communicate the way they do. The theories also help people in the discipline to predict what will happen when someone communicates in a particular way. For example, if you talk and behave in a hostile way to another person, what kind of reaction do you expect from the other person? Clearly, the other person's reaction depends on whether he or she thought you were serious, how he or she felt at the time, what he or she thought the consequences might be, and possibly many other conditions. One theory suggests that the other person will react to you in a hostile way; that is, if you are nasty to someone, that person will be nasty to you.

How do we find out whether this theory predicts people's behavior accurately? The answer is: Do some research! That is, try out your hostile attitude on someone and closely observe what he or she does. If the person does react in a hostile manner, you would feel that the theory predicted the reaction fairly well. If the other person reacted in a sweet and gentle way, you would probably wonder why. Did the tone of your voice give you away so that the other person thought you were only kidding? Did the other person feel sorry for you and just disregard your hostile behavior as unusual at the moment? If any of these attitudes prevailed, you would not be able to depend on the theory to predict people's behavior. But if these attitudes were held constant, you might have been able to predict quite accurately what would have happened.

The point is that in answering questions when using scientific research, you must be able to exercise some control over the kinds of things said and done, to whom they are said, and the manner in which they are done. Otherwise, you will not be able to determine whether your particular behavior or statement was the one to which the other person reacted. Conducting research requires being able to define what you are interested in finding out. The process of creating definitions and

1

making decisions about variables is like developing *a game plan,* which is applicable to conducting all scientific research. Thus, we have created the *If-Then Game* to guide you through the steps of research in the science of communication in a systematic but also painless and elementary way. Study this game to grasp the general way in which research is conducted. You will find that each of the studies and experiments described in this manual was developed by following the format of the If-Then Game. Look for the similarities.

The If-Then Game:
A Systematic Approach to Planning
and Conducting Research

Scientific research can be likened to playing a game like *Monopoly.* We have a notion of what we must do to win the game. We are aware that to win we must proceed through a series of rule-governed stops and goes and return situations until we purchase as much property as possible and cause our opponents to go bankrupt. As we analyze the game, we are very much aware that an incorrect move can cause us to lose or not do well. This is much like scientific research. We must proceed systematically through a set of rules, always keeping alert to avoid as many stops and returns as possible while increasing the number of goes. If we look at the objective of the *If-Then Game* as the discovery of new information rather than the purchase of property, we will put our sights on a truly exciting goal. Research is much like *Monopoly* in that a move may represent either a conquest or a pitfall. Each satisfactorily completed move brings about a feeling of excitement and confidence, but each pitfall makes us have to retrace our steps or begin the game all over again. This constant process of starting, stopping, or returning to an earlier stage or moving ahead represents the overall feeling of what research is all about. Effective research is progressing systematically to the end of the game, realizing that mistakes may cause us to lose or require us to take another avenue to complete the game.

The following "game" is the one we play as we perform each experiment in this manual. The game should prove helpful to us in discovering and recognizing those steps which should be systematically followed to do good research. There are trouble spots that should be carefully avoided; they will become evident as we play the game. The game does not purport to give us complete knowledge about scientific research; but if it whets your appetite for further study, you might want to read Bowers' *Designing the Communication Experiment.*[1]

The research game is divided into four areas: I. *The Question;* II. *Literature Search;* III. *Research Development;* and IV. *Data Collection and Outcomes.* To complete the game, the research must progress sequentially through each of these four areas, and each one has a system of steps that must be completed before a researcher can proceed to the next area. Begin the game in the upper left-hand corner with the words "Start Here." The rules for each step in the game are as follows:

[1]John Waite Bowers, *Designing the Communication Experiment* (New York: Random House, 1970).

I. The Question

1. *Thinking and Fooling Around*   This might seem like a silly way to begin a game that deals with research. However, some of our most provocative ideas come from interacting with others, eating apples, watching dust settle out of the air, and just plain daydreaming. As you are living, you may have feelings of frustration about the ways people respond to you. If you sense a clear problem now, advance three spaces to Step Four.

2. *Getting an Idea*   Out of that frustration, you may start to ask questions about *why* you are treated as you are. As these questions begin to germinate, you will find yourself at Step Two. Many of us lose the research game by never progressing to this step. We daydream, but we never really get ideas. In fact, Step One is where many good ideas stay; they never get started, and we never finish the game. As you raise questions about your relationships with others, or anything else for that matter, you are ready to move to Step Three. You should not hold your thoughts forever; you must act upon them. But if nothing specific has developed by now, you must return to Step One. Or, as Einstein and Infeld put it:

> The formulation of a problem is far more often essential than its solution, which may be merely a matter of mathematical or experimental skill. To raise new questions, new possibilities, to regard old problems from a new angle requires creative imagination and marks real advance in science.[2]

3. *Question*   Now you must ask yourself, what is it that I wish to know about the idea? What specific questions do I want to answer? When you know exactly what relationships you wish to understand, then you are prepared to progress to Step Four. If you are unclear, lose one turn, and go back one space to Step Two.

4. *Statement*   You must now state a specific focus concerning the idea. You write down clearly and succinctly your specific purpose. That is, you must state, for example, that you are interested in discovering whether humor affects attitude change. If you can state very specifically what you are searching for, then you may advance three spaces to Step Six. However, if you have difficulty stating specifically what you want to discover, then you may advance one space to Step Five.

5. *Worthwhile*   If you cannot state the idea specifically, then maybe you do not really know what you are looking for. Answering the question "What can information on this idea help us understand about communication?" may help to determine whether the idea is valuable and provide a guide to stating it specifically. If not, then you should go back four spaces to Step One *(Thinking and Fooling Around)* and begin the game again. If you feel the idea is of worth but the question is still not specific, then lose only two spaces and return to Step Three *(Question)* to reconsider what question you are really trying to answer.

6. *Clarity*   After you have a specific and worthwhile question to answer, advance to Step Six where you ask yourself the following questions: Is the statement of the

---

[2]Albert Einstein and Leopold Infeld, *The Evolution of Physics* (New York: Simon and Schuster, 1938); taken from Stephen Isaac and William B. Michael, *Handbook in Research and Evaluation* (San Diego: Robert R. Knapp, Publisher, 1972), p. 1.

The "If-Then" Game

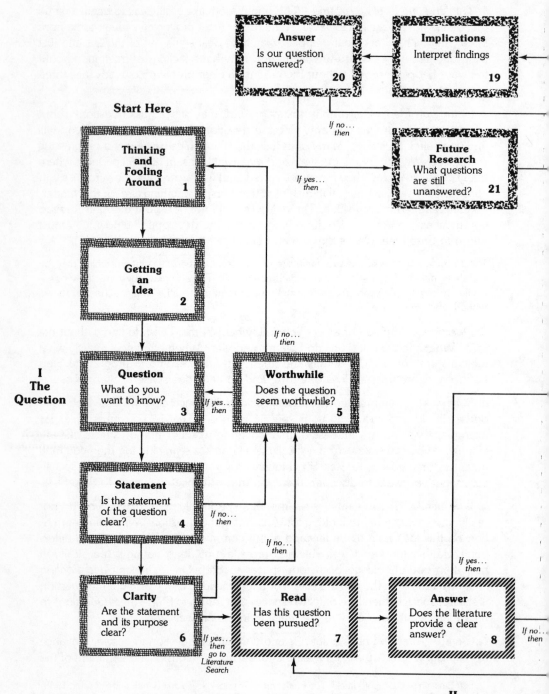

Answer
Is our question answered? **20**

Implications
Interpret findings **19**

Future Research
What questions are still unanswered? **21**

Start Here

Thinking and Fooling Around **1**

Getting an Idea **2**

I
The Question

Question
What do you want to know? **3**

Worthwhile
Does the question seem worthwhile? **5**

Statement
Is the statement of the question clear? **4**

Clarity
Are the statement and its purpose clear? **6**

Read
Has this question been pursued? **7**

Answer
Does the literature provide a clear answer? **8**

If no... then

If yes... then

If no... then

If yes... then

If no... then

If no... then

If yes... then

If yes... then go to Literature Search

If no... then

II
Literature Search

4

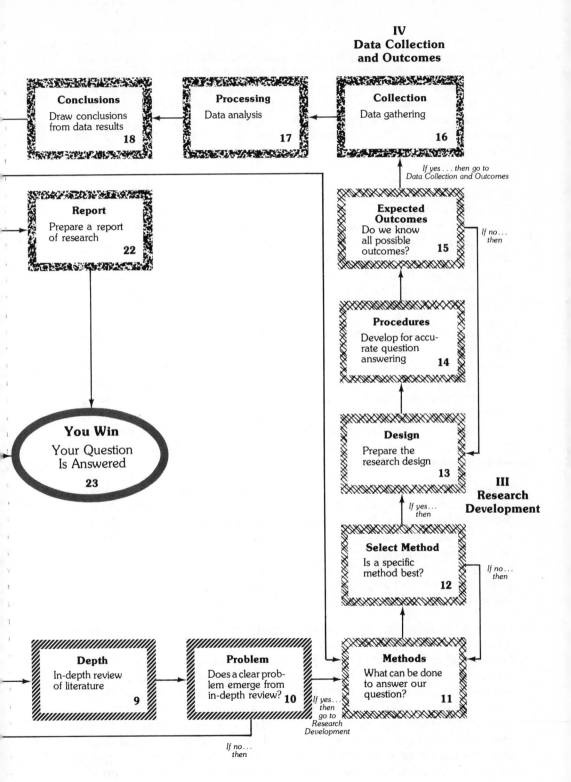

IV
Data Collection
and Outcomes

Conclusions
Draw conclusions
from data results
18

Processing
Data analysis
17

Collection
Data gathering
16

If yes . . . then go to
Data Collection and Outcomes

Report
Prepare a report
of research
22

Expected
Outcomes
Do we know
all possible
outcomes? **15**

If no . . .
then

Procedures
Develop for accu-
rate question
answering **14**

You Win
Your Question
Is Answered
23

Design
Prepare the
research design
13

III
Research
Development

If yes . . .
then

Select Method
Is a specific
method best?
12

If no . . .
then

Depth
In-depth review
of literature
9

Problem
Does a clear prob-
lem emerge from
in-depth review? **10**

If yes . . .
then
go to
Research
Development

Methods
What can be done
to answer our
question? **11**

If no . . .
then

idea and its purpose clear? (Do I really know what I am seeking?) Is the question and the potential answer going to be worthwhile? If the first question is answered in the negative, lose two turns and go back two spaces to Step Four, and restate the question more clearly. If the second question is answered in the negative, go back one space and reevaluate the worth of the question again. If both questions are answered positively, move forward one space and begin Part II of the game, *Literature Search*.

II. Literature Search

7. *Read*   Go to the library and read as many sources as you can find to determine if your idea has been studied already. As you read, ask yourself: Has this question been pursued? If someone else has reported a study on the question, determine where it is similar and different from what you had in mind. Read broadly; it might surprise you where you will find research reported on related questions. After you have read widely and made a record of relevant research done in the area, then advance one space to Step Eight.

8. *Answer*   After you have read widely, you must ask yourself this question: Does the literature provide a clear answer? Has someone discovered the answer to the question? If you determine that someone has done the research and answered your question, then *they win the game!* You need not proceed through any more steps or do your own scientific research, for someone else has found an answer. Do nothing more than go to Step Twenty-Three—the game's end—and scream "Hallelujah" (quietly). However, most of your questions will not be answered very well by the research of other people. When you find that a clear answer is not provided, proceed to Step Nine.

9. *Depth*   At this point you must complete an in-depth critical analysis of the literature to determine why there is no clear-cut answer to your question. You may discover that your question has never been raised in precisely the way you have. It may be that your question was precisely stated but poorly answered. It may be that the research provides conflicting answers. The available research must be analyzed to determine why the question has not been answered adequately. If you cannot figure out why no answer exists, lose two turns, return to Step Eight, and go back to the library; you have probably missed something.

10. *Problem*   When you decide why the question has not been answered, usually a clearer and more specific problem begins to emerge. If after in-depth research has taken place and a critical problem has not emerged, then you must go back two spaces to Step Seven and begin the *Literature Search* again. If a clear problem emerges, then you may progress to the third area of the game, *Research Development*. You should keep in mind that as you review the literature, occasionally a more basic question appears than the one you were asking with your original idea. You should not be dismayed by this since the more fundamental questions are often more exciting and productive anyway. Consider the discovery of a new problem to be a breakthrough, give yourself four widgets, and advance to Part III.

III. Research Development

11. *Methods*   Your first task is to determine what research methods are best suited to studying your question. Should you use the empirical method? What about the possibility of the historical method? Should you consider a critical study? Or you may decide to use a combination of all of these methods. A discussion of other methods can be found in the text section that goes with this manual. When you have considered all possible methods for use in your study, you may proceed to Step Twelve.

12. *Method Selection*   Which of the many possible methods is best for answering the specific question you posed? If you can determine the best method, then move to Step Thirteen. If you cannot determine the best method, go back a space to Step Eleven, and review the literature on research to discover if there are other methods that could be used for this problem.

13. *Design*   After you have selected a research method, begin to design the research plan—exactly how the study will be conducted. You must determine those techniques that will help answer the question most directly and precisely. This is accomplished by making one move forward to Step Fourteen.

14. *Procedures*   The procedures are the specifics of the design. You need to decide who the subjects will be and how they will be tested, and where and under what conditions the data will be collected. You need to describe, in as much detail as possible, a step-by-step account of what will transpire during the actual data collection and preparation. You must develop the best possible sequence for conducting the study so that you can have confidence that the question posed can be answered.

15. *Expected Outcomes*   Prior to doing the actual research, you must try to explain all of the possible outcomes of the research. What will happen if the results are in the opposite direction from those expected? What if the results support your expectations? If you have not accounted for all possible types of outcomes in your design and procedures, then you must go back two spaces to Step Thirteen and reevaluate the design and procedures. If you feel that all possible outcomes have been identified, then you may move one space forward to the final area of the game, *Data Collection and Outcomes.*

IV. Data Collection and Outcomes

16. *Collection*   This is simply the process of collecting data according to the predetermined procedures. When all the data are collected, you may move to Step Seventeen.

17. *Processing*   According to established procedures, you tabulate and calculate the data to obtain results. When finished, move ahead one space.

18. *Conclusions*   Analyze the obtained results, and determine what kinds of conclusions are justified in light of these results. As soon as the conclusions are stated clearly and precisely, proceed to Step Nineteen.

19. *Implications* At this point, the study is finished. However, before you put the sandbags away and tear down the walls, consider what you have learned that might suggest new studies. What other questions have been raised by the research you were doing? When you have several ideas written down, take one move forward to Step Twenty.

20. *Answer* Have you answered the question which was spawned by the original idea? If your answer is no, then you can do either of two things: (1) Return to Step Eleven, and develop a new research design in hopes of receiving a better and more efficient answer to your question; or (2) give up, move on to Step Twenty-One, and discuss the need for future research. If your answer is yes, you should progress immediately to Step Twenty-One and discuss what questions are still unanswered and what questions you feel need further research. Move one space forward.

21. *Future Research* Now answer questions like these: What questions are left unanswered? Where do we go from here? What research still needs to be done? Move one space forward.

22. *Report* The final step prior to winning the game is the reporting of results. For research to be meaningful, for it to allow others to avoid going over the same questions, and for it to allow for research to build systematically upon what has already been done, you need to write a report of your work. The report should include the question pursued, the literature reviewed, the way the methods and procedures were developed, how the data were collected, the results obtained, and the recommendations for further research. After completing the written report, you have completed the research game. If you have honestly and diligently followed the steps of the game in a systematic fashion, then the reward you receive is not just the completion of the game but also the knowledge that you have done effective and meaningful research and discovered new information.

23. *You Win!* Your question is answered.

Once the game is completed and the collected data are available for others to read and evaluate, you have begun to contribute to a science. As you study and conduct experiments in this manual, refer back to this game. Follow the steps in the game, and identify where the experiments you are working with could be more effective. As more research is completed in the area of human communication behavior and as studies begin to build upon one another, the area of study we call communicology will become a science. As you read, perform, and analyze the studies in this manual, we hope that you will attempt to develop questions and ideas that will cause you to explore new areas of communication behavior and that you will become part of the developing science of communication behavior.

Theory

Scientific research has as its main objective to describe what is happening now or has happened in the past to help establish a basis for constructing theories that will accurately predict happenings in the future. The combined purpose of making accurate observations and statements is to describe communicative behavior in as true and as orderly a scheme as possible. This means that we should be able to make statements that predict what will happen under certain communicative circumstances. Initially, we call these somewhat predictable statements *theory*. Theory allows us to forecast how certain people will behave when exposed to a specific kind of message. If the statements continue to forecast human behavior accurately, then they are no longer merely a theory but become facts or truth. On the other hand, when a theory is tested and the predicted consequences do not occur, then we begin to doubt the statements and to question whether they represent the facts. If we continue to observe consequences that the theory does not predict, then we must change the theory. The purpose of scientific inquiry is not to stipulate what *should happen* but to describe *what has happened* in order to predict what will happen in the future.

Unfortunately, as we have discovered many times, it is very difficult, if not entirely impossible, to describe and specify all of the circumstances influencing what we observe. The willingness to accept this inability to account for every variable in a situation is an attitude that should characterize all those who engage in scientific research. Suppose you ask a prominent communicator how to get people to accept what you say. You follow his suggestions, but your audience rejects your appeals. As a scientist, what should be your attitude? Under such circumstances, the best attitude is one of tentativeness. A communicologist should wonder whether the advice of a prominent communicator that does not get the predicted results actually represents truthful statements. A communicologist should submit the communicator's suggestions to a test. That is, he or she should create an experiment in an effort to discover what results might be expected from presenting a particular message to a particular audience under certain circumstances. Then, the communicologist should create just those kinds of circumstances and meticulously observe the communicative behavior in the situation. Finally, the communicologist should describe very carefully what took place, keeping in mind how the results might lead to a more accurate prediction for future happenings. If the information derived from the observations seems inadequate to make very accurate predictions, the communicologist should offer his suggestions with tentativeness or avoid making any suggestions at all.

If a communicologist does not have evidence to support a particular prediction, he should have the honesty to say so. Communicologists, much to the dismay of the uninformed, are completely dedicated to discovering truth; as we have previously indicated, the truth about a matter lies in what actually happens —the facts. One of the difficulties with accepting a scientific frame of mind is that we must commit ourselves to accepting the truth even when it is opposed to our own desires. T. H. Huxley related to this difficulty when he stated: "The tragedies of science are the slaying of beautiful hypotheses by ugly facts."

Honesty ought to be the most important characteristic of a communicologist. Regretfully, human beings who purport to engage in scientific activities are often no more honest than other people, for they are subject to the same kinds of human errors as others. They have their own desires, wants, and private expectations. Nevertheless, scientific procedures have been developed that help ensure the accuracy of information obtained by scientists. If the procedures reported do not conform to the rigors of the *If-Then Game,* you may have reason to doubt their accuracy.

Using Statistics

To complete the research studies in this manual, it is not necessary to have a knowledge of statistics. The manipulations of data in this manual can be done by following the step-by-step directions with each experiment. If you feel a need to do a more sophisticated statistical analysis of the obtained data, then you must have a knowledge of statistics. If that is the case, ask your instructor for advice.

Try not to have an unwarranted fear of statistics, for statistics are merely tools to use to analyze data. They simply tell us the probability of obtaining the same results each time we replicate the study. If you wish to gain a greater understanding of statistics, we recommend that you read any statistics book recommended by your instructor or another faculty member familiar with statistical methods.

Research and People: Ethical Considerations

When doing research with human beings, we must keep a number of ethical considerations in mind. It is absolutely crucial that we are satisfied that we are not hurting the subjects in any way. Experimenters do not have the right to abuse people who volunteer to serve as subjects. The following guidelines should be minimally observed when using human subjects.

1.   In considering the participation of humans as subjects, keep in mind that no one should be expected to risk his or her health or well-being without being given all reasonable protection and without being adequately informed.

2.   In general, the purpose of the study, the procedures to be followed, and the possible risks involved must be explained to the subject. The researcher must be satisfied that the explanation has been understood and that consent was obtained without duress or deception. Such an explanation may be postponed or even omitted when the researcher judges that there are no risks to the subject and when a full account of the purpose and procedure in advance might bias the results.

3.   It is the responsibility of the individual researcher to have adequate knowledge of the possible consequences of his research or of research done under his direction.

4.   The subject's personal privacy and the confidentiality of information received from him must be protected.

5.   A subject's time should not be invaded to the extent that his participation creates conflict with his other obligations.

6.   Any subject may request termination of his participation at any time, and his request should be honored promptly and without prejudice.

There are many aspects of research ethics that one must keep in mind as research is done with people. The ideas just listed are not comprehensive; in fact, they may omit some important aspects from your point of view. As you do the research in this manual and as you think about the way you like to be treated by researchers, you should formulate a set of ethics that you can work with and that will not be detrimental to the people with whom you work.

Using This Manual

A laboratory manual is a tool to be mauled, mangled, and marked. Whereas the text section provides explanations about theory, this manual provides directions for the discovery of information and contains space for you to write your own statements about what you discover about ideas and concepts.

This manual describes the steps to be taken in order to conduct the experiments. Your instructor may conduct an experiment during the class period, you may be asked to conduct an experiment outside of the class, or you and the instructor may work together in conducting an experiment that begins in class but continues outside of class. In any case, you should carefully record and tabulate the data and write out results, conclusions, and implications for applying the results in your day-to-day communication. Spaces are provided in the manual for making a record of not only the raw data and the results but also the step-by-step procedures and physical setup used by the person conducting the experiment. You should make it a regular practice to take careful notes about each of the experiments presented in class; these notes will aid you in understanding how to conduct an experiment so that you will be able to conduct your own experiments outside of class. It may be a good idea to sketch right in the manual a diagram showing how each experiment was set up and handled when it was presented in class.

No one can be expected to conduct an experiment without having planned it. Although the manual does much of the preparation for you, you must be familiar with all the principles and research procedures of each experiment before beginning. This means that you need to study the text section to have some understanding of the propositions and research related to them. In addition, you will need to review the experiment to be conducted in order to be familiar with the materials and procedures in advance. The better informed you are, the easier it will be to conduct and understand the experiments.

The experiments are designed to challenge you to learn about communication behavior in an exciting and unique way. As a matter of fact, you may become so intrigued with the scientific approach to learning about communication that you will want to create and conduct an experiment of your own rather than replicating research done by others; you will find few things that bring more satisfaction. Keep in mind, however, that faculty, as well as students, must have approval to proceed with research. So, never attempt to conduct an unauthorized experiment. Always contact your instructor, and secure approval to design and conduct experiments. In addition, your instructor may have some new ideas and good suggestions to aid you in producing a successful experiment.

Part 1
Experiments about Relationships

Chapter 1
Interpersonal Dynamics

The basic unit of interaction with which we are now concerned is called person-to-person or *dyadic* communication. Most studies of the dynamics of interpersonal relationships are concerned with dyads; and the common feature of dyadic communication is that one individual establishes an emotional connection with another. The experiments that follow are concerned with factors that influence the dyadic interactive process—the most prominent variables being self-disclosure, empathy, warmth, acceptance, openness, supportiveness, trust, and mutual need-satisfaction.

Experiment 1.1
Expressions of Warmth

Proposition
An effective interpersonal relationship occurs when both parties express a warm, positive attitude toward each other.

Research Questions
Do people tend to talk more willingly with another person when the other reacts with warmth?

Does warmth have a reinforcing influence on verbal behavior?

Do nonverbal expressions of warmth and reinforcing language responses, when occurring together, have an even greater influence on verbalizations?

Research Methods*

Subjects

Four naive respondees who are not members of this class.

One trained reinforcer, who may be a member of this class.

Materials

Two tape recorders with reel and tape or cassette for recording the interviews and playing back the recordings for data tabulation.

Copies of Tabulation Sheet for recording the frequencies of words.

One stopwatch or clock with a sweep second hand.

Procedures

1. Selection and Preparation of Subjects
    a. Ask four individuals who are not members of this class to participate in the experiment. Give them very little information concerning the purpose of the experiment; they will be the *respondees*.
    b. Select a member of the class to serve as the *experimenter*. Meet with the experimenter to explain the research procedures and to provide training in the required reinforcing behaviors. The experiment will be conducted in four parts.
        (1) During parts 1 and 2, the experimenter is to reinforce plural nouns (*people, men, women, horses,* etc.) verbally by saying "mm-hmm," "good," or "fine" immediately after a respondee utters a plural noun.
        (2) Verbal reinforcement should take place under two different conditions—nonverbal *warmth* and nonverbal *coldness*.
            (a) In the warm condition, the experimenter is to lean toward and look directly at the subject, to smile but avoid moving his or her hands while giving the verbal reinforcement.
            (b) In the cold condition, the experimenter is to lean away from the subject, look around the room rather than at the subject, avoid smiling, and then drum the fingers of either or both hands while giving the verbal reinforcement.
            (c) The verbal utterances should be maintained continuously throughout the experimental period.
        (3) Parts 3 and 4 will consist of having the experimenter express warmth and coldness without providing any verbal reinforcement.
        (4) During the experiment, the experimenter should do no talking except to give instructions and verbal reinforcement, depending on which condition is being tested.
2. Conduct of the Experiment
    a. Place a microphone leading to the tape recorder between the respondee

*Adapted from an experiment reported in Michael M. Reece and Robert N. Whitman, "Expressive Movements, Warmth, and Verbal Reinforcement," *Journal of Abnormal and Social Psychology*, Vol. 64, (1962) pp. 234-236. Copyright 1962 by the American Psychological Association. By permission.

and the experimenter so that the statements of the respondee are recorded clearly.

b. The experimenter explains to the respondee that he or she is to engage in a 10-minute period of free association. The respondee is to say whatever words come to mind during the 10-minute period. Each word is to be said individually. Please do not use phrases or numbers. This procedure is to be repeated under four different conditions:

Warm nonverbal with verbal reinforcement

Cold nonverbal with verbal reinforcement

Warm nonverbal reinforcement

Cold nonverbal reinforcement

A different subject–respondee should be used for each condition.

c. For both warm and cold verbal and nonverbal reinforcement conditions, the experimenter is to exhibit the appropriate behaviors and to reinforce plural nouns by saying "mm-hmm," "good," or "fine." For both warm and cold nonverbal reinforcement conditions, the experimenter will simply exhibit the appropriate behavior without uttering verbal reinforcements.

d. At the end of 10 minutes, each respondee should be thanked, and the next respondee should be brought to the experimental area and the next condition completed.

3. Tabulation of the Data

a. After completing each interview, a committee of class members should take each tape recording to another room.

   (1) The tape should be played on the second tape recorder and a tabulation made of the number of plural nouns and the total number of words uttered.

   (2) Part of the committee could count plural nouns, and part could count the total number of words.

b. Tally the number of plural nouns and the total number of words for each condition on the Tabulation Sheet, page 21. Record the totals in the appropriate boxes below.

	Number of Words Uttered	
	Nouns	Total
Warm: Verbal and Nonverbal		
Warm: Nonverbal Only		
Cold: Verbal and Nonverbal		
Cold: Nonverbal Only		

Name _____   Section _____

Date _____   Instructor _____

Results

1. Which of the conditions produced the greatest number of words?

2. Which of the conditions produced the greatest number of plural nouns?

3. Did verbal reinforcement influence the total number of words spoken?

4. Was verbal reinforcement sufficient to produce an increase in plural nouns?

5. Did the expressive movements (warm and cold) successfully convey the attitudes indicated?

6. Did the expressive movements have an effect on the total number of words spoken?

Explanation

1. Write a concise summary of this experiment and the results obtained.

2.   What conclusions can be drawn from this experiment about the effects of expressions of warmth on interpersonal interaction?

Tabulation Sheet

Conditions	Total Number of Words Uttered	Number of Plural Nouns Uttered
Warm: Verbal and Nonverbal		
Warm: Nonverbal Only		
Cold: Verbal and Nonverbal		
Cold: Nonverbal Only		

Experiment 1.2
Interpersonal Hostility

Proposition

An effective interpersonal relationship occurs when both parties perceive each other as maintaining an open and supportive climate.

Research Questions

Does the communication of hostility through overt aggressive behavior directed toward another person tend to reduce feelings of hostility toward that person?

Do overt acts of aggression in response to the instigation of hostility tend to reduce the level of hostility in the aggressor? Does thwarting of communication back to an instigator of hostility tend to increase the level of hostility?

Research Methods*

Subjects

Four naive diagnosers who are *not* members of this class.

Four diagnosers who are members of this class.

Four messengers who are members of this class.

Materials

Six free-standing panels or portable blackboards to separate the eight diagnosers (*see diagram, page 24*).

Eight small tables and eight chairs.

Paper and pencils for writing messages.

Content Analysis Coding Sheet.

Standard Notes for Informed Diagnoser (make 8 copies for each informed diagnoser).

Procedures

1. Selection and Preparation of Subjects
   a. Ask the naive subjects to appear at the experimental area at a precise time; a pair of informed subjects (a diagnoser and a messenger assigned in advance) will meet them there. The informed subjects should rehearse their roles but pretend to be naive about the purpose of the study; they should not be personally acquainted with the naive subjects.
   b. Subjects should be assigned to cubicles, created by free-standing partitions, with alternating naive and informed diagnosers (four on each side of the experimental area). A naive diagnoser should be paired with an

---

*Adapted from an experiment reported in John W. Thibaut and John Coules, "The Role of Communication in the Reduction of Interpersonal Hostility," *Journal of Abnormal and Social Psychology,* Vol. 47 (1952), pp. 770-777. Copyright 1952 by the American Psychological Association. By permission.

informed diagnoser, but with each in his or her own small room in which to work. The diagnosers should be seated at tables facing each other so that they are in constant view of the other at all times.

Other Members of Class

Front of Room

   c.   The two diagnosers will communicate with one another by writing notes about themselves, and the messenger will deliver the messages.

   d.   The experimenter will explain that this is an attempt to determine whether undergraduate students can learn as much about one another's personalities by direct communication as a professional counselor could working from test materials.

2. Conduct of the Experiment

   a.   At this point, the experimenter should designate the naive subject as a diagnoser and appear to select arbitrarily one of the informed subjects as the other diagnoser. The remaining informed subject is assigned the job of messenger. The diagnosers are to go to their cubicles.

   b.   Before proceeding with the message exchanges, each diagnoser is instructed to write an initial "personality sketch" consisting of his or her *first impressions* of the other diagnoser. The informed diagnoser need only pretend to write a sketch.

   c.   As soon as the naive diagnoser has finished the sketch, begin the communication process, bearing in mind two restrictions:

      (1) All messages must be in the form of written notes.

      (2) The content of the notes must refer to his or her self.

     Use the following instructions:

We would like to have you go on now and write notes to each other. You can write as many notes as you wish. Here is some paper you can use. Write about yourself, telling the other person whatever you want to about your personality, your ambitions, your likes and dislikes, telling as much as you can, so that at the end, the other person will be able to write a better personality sketch of you. When you've finished writing a note, rap on the table and the messenger will come up and deliver it. As soon as you receive a note, read it right away. Don't let the notes pile up.

d. The informed diagnoser should initiate a standard set of eight notes at intervals of two minutes each.
   (1) The first seven are intended to characterize the informed diagnoser as arrogant and opinionated but not "strong" enough to inhibit aggression from the naive diagnoser.
   (2) The eighth note is calculated to act as the instigation of hostility. This note ignores the instructions to write only about one's self and states a strong denunciation of the naive diagnoser.

e. Two of the naive diagnosers should be permitted to send one additional note after receiving the eighth-instigator note, and two of the naive diagnosers should not be permitted to do so. This can be accomplished in this way: As soon as the no-communication diagnoser has finished reading the eighth note, enter the cubicle and announce that the allotted time is up. Allow the other diagnosers to write one additional note after the instigation. When it is delivered, step into the cubicle and terminate the time.

f. At the conclusion of the note-exchange period, each of the diagnosers should write a final personality sketch of his or her partner (have the informed diagnoser pretend). As soon as the naive diagnosers have finished, informally interview all of the diagnosers about how they feel about the task.

g. Bring all of the participants together, and explain the nature of the experiment; extend apologies and request a cessation of hostilities.

3. Tabulation of the Data
   a. Content analyses should be completed separately for the preexperimental personality sketch and the postexperimental sketch written by the naive diagnoser. The sketches should be analyzed in terms of four general categories of content:
      (1) Hostile statements—include any wish, fantasy, or intention to commit a destructive act; attribution of an undesirable characteristic or denial of a desirable characteristic to instigator; direct expression of hostile feeling toward instigator; statements that represent negative modeling (not wanting to be like the instigator) and statements of strong disagreement.
      (2) Neutral statements—include statements that reflect neither positive nor negative feelings.
      (3) Friendly statements—include all references to the instigator as an object to be admired, liked, or modeled; attribution of favorable characteristics.
      (4) General and miscellaneous statements—include all comments having no apparent reference to the instigator.
   b. In coding the personality sketches, consider each sentence as a unit. However, when a change in category occurs within a sentence, both categories should be scored, each as a separate unit.

c. Coding can be accomplished by dividing the class into committees. Depending on the number of committees, these codings can be used:
    (1) Prepersonality sketches of communication diagnosers.
    (2) Postpersonality sketches of communication diagnosers.
    (3) Presketches of noncommunication diagnosers.
    (4) Postsketches of noncommunication diagnosers.
d. Tabulate the total number of units analyzed in each of the sketches.

	Presketches	Postsketches
S1		
S2		
S3		
S4		

e. Calculate the percentage of hostile, neutral, friendly, and miscellaneous units included in the presketch and the postsketch.

		Presketch	Postsketch
S1 (comm)	Hostile		
	Neutral		
	Friendly		
	Misc.		
S2 (comm)	Hostile		
	Neutral		
	Friendly		
	Misc.		
S3 (noncomm)	Hostile		
	Neutral		
	Friendly		
	Misc.		
S4 (noncomm)	Hostile		
	Neutral		
	Friendly		
	Misc.		

Name _____ Section _____

Date _____ Instructor _____

Results

1. Which sketch (pre or post) yielded the largest number of hostile and friendly units?

2. Which condition (comm or noncomm) produced the largest number of hostile and friendly units?

3. Which combination (pre/post, comm/noncomm) yielded the largest number of hostile and friendly units?

4. What other similarities and differences seem to occur between the four conditions (pre/post, comm/noncomm)?

5. What effect did being able to communicate an additional message have upon the expression of hostility in the postsketches?

6. Does the number of friendly units or the number of hostile units yield the greatest amount of information about the effects of being able to communicate hostility to an instigator of hostility?

Explanation

1. Write a concise summary of this experiment and the results obtained.

2. What conclusions can be drawn from this experiment about the effects of being able to talk back to an instigator of hostility?

3. What do the results of this experiment suggest about the effects of an open and supportive climate on interpersonal relationships?

Content Analysis Coding Sheet

		Presketch	Postsketch
S 1 (comm)	Hostile Units		
	Neutral Units		
	Friendly Units		
	Misc. Units		
	Total Units		
S 2 (comm)	Hostile Units		
	Neutral Units		
	Friendly Units		
	Misc. Units		
	Total Units		
S 3 (noncomm)	Hostile Units		
	Neutral Units		
	Friendly Units		
	Misc. Units		
	Total Units		
S 4 (noncomm)	Hostile Units		
	Neutral Units		
	Friendly Units		
	Misc. Units		
	Total Units		

Standard Notes for Informed Diagnoser

1. I was a very talented child. I won the county spelling bee and scored highest on elementary school English tests. I was always chosen first on school baseball teams. I knew that I would be a top student right from the beginning.

2. I had a music teacher a few years back who said I was a prodigy. As I think about it, she was right. I don't play the clarinet as well as I could. All I need to do is practice. I have natural talent in music as well as other areas.

3. I know I'll succeed in my profession because I am so far above everybody else in my class. I got 98 on my last biology exam, and that's pretty good. I am the best student in the lab course also.

4. If I might say so myself, the women (or men) prefer my company to just about everyone else. Along with my brilliant intellect, my superior good looks always impresses them. I once had four women (or men) asking me to go out with them. Of course, I chose the best looking and the most sophisticated. None of the others would feel comfortable around me.

5. I do not have much time for people who are stupid. They dissipate my energy and waste the efforts of an outstanding individual. I once told off one of the faculty members for making a silly mistake in a math course. She deserved it.

6. Not enough people know how to handle difficult situations. I never make mistakes. People should consult with me more often before they decide what kind of car to buy. I'm a whiz at identifying great bargains. I always save the most on jewelry. I really know how to find the right people.

7. Since I am kind of weak, I haven't been good in any sports—but that's just kid stuff; I want to be a *man* (or *woman*). I am sure if I wanted to be a good athlete, I would be *very* successful even though I don't care much for physical contact of that sort.

8. You know, you're so full of bull——, that I'm not going to talk about myself anymore. You're the most egotistical, deceitful *liar* I've ever seen. How anybody can fake about his own abilities as much as you have, I'll never know. I don't think you're the type of person I'd care to associate with. Why don't you play it straight?

Chapter 2
Improving Relationships

Most effective interpersonal relationships do not happen by accident; they develop through applications of principles of communication by means of skills that facilitate fulfilling relationships. Openness, trust, warmth, liking, accuracy of understanding, genuineness, and helpful response methods represent some of the ways of behaving that tend to improve interpersonal relationships.

Experiment 2.1
Self-Disclosure and Trust

Proposition

Interpersonal relationships tend to improve when both parties communicate information about each other's private world through self-disclosure.

Research Questions

Will a person trust another more when the other responds to the person's self-disclosures with acceptance rather than when the other responds with rejection?

Will a person trust the other more when the other reciprocates the person's self-disclosures rather than when the other does not?

Research Methods*

Subjects
Eight naive subjects who are not members of this class.

Four confederates who are members of this class.

*Adapted from an experiment reported in David W. Johnson and M. Patricia Noonan, "Effects of Acceptance and Reciprocation of Self-Disclosures on the Development of Trust," *Journal of Counseling Psychology,* Vol. 19 (1972), pp. 411-416. By permission.

Materials

Four scripts or short speeches: 2 favoring legalized abortion (1 containing personal arguments and 1 containing impersonal arguments); 2 opposing legalized abortion (1 containing personal arguments and 1 containing impersonal arguments).

Preexperimental Opinion Questionnaire for each naive subject (8 copies).

Two briefing sheets containing arguments (4 copies of each).

Instruction Sheet for Research Sessions (4 copies).

Postexperimental Opinion Questionnaire (8 copies).

Postexperimental Attitude Scales (8 copies).

Procedures

1. Selection and Preparation of Subjects
   a. Orientation and training of confederates
      (1) Two confederates will be trained to express acceptance and rejection and will memorize script speeches containing arguments—one in support of legalized abortion (Script 1) and one opposed to it (Script 3)—of a *personal* nature. Following the presentation of his or her position, the confederate makes self-disclosing statements *after* the subject does so. This creates a reciprocal self-disclosing relationship.

      Acceptance: In this condition, the confederate should behave in a caring and warm way but never agree with the subject's position. Verbal statements such as "I understand," "I see how you feel," "That's an interesting point" are to be used. Nonverbally, the confederate is to smile, use a warm and interested tone of voice, use direct eye contact, lean toward the subject, and, in general, look interested in what the subject is saying. Twice during the discussion, the confederate should say, "I understand how you feel although I don't agree with you."

      Rejection: In this condition, the confederate should behave in cold and disinterested ways. He or she should interrupt the subject, make statements such as "That doesn't make sense," "You're kidding," "I could never agree with that," or "I don't see how anyone could really believe that." The confederate should make rejecting statements nearing personal affront. Nonverbally, the confederate should turn away from the subject, get up and walk away, shrug, raise hands in disagreement and surprise, doodle, stare at the subject, make disinterested and disagreeing facial expressions, and use a cold tone of voice.

      (2) Two confederates will be trained to express acceptance and rejection (*see above*) and will memorize script speeches containing arguments—one in support of legalized abortion (Script 2) and one opposed to it (Script 4)—of an *impersonal* nature. Confederates should *not* provide self-disclosure.
   b. Ask the eight naive subjects to arrive at the experimental area at a specific time. Arrange to have four of the subjects wait in an adjoining area where they will not be exposed to the experimental procedures.
   c. Explain to the remaining subjects that part of the task will be to prepare

some arguments to support their position on legalized abortion (favor or oppose). They will be assigned a partner with the same opinion; but in order to do so, it will be necessary to indicate his or her opinion. Have each subject check the appropriate statement on a two-item Preexperimental Opinion Questionnaire:

☐ I favor legalizing abortion.

☐ I oppose legalizing abortion.

    d.   Collect the questionnaires, and have each subject escorted to an individual cubicle or small room.
    e.   Have a confederate who has been informed of the stated opinion of the subject join him or her as a person of the same opinion.
    f.   Explain privately to each pair that two other individuals of opposing opinions are meeting in another area, preparing arguments to support their position.
    g.   Distribute to each pair a briefing sheet outlining four arguments that support their stated position. In addition, give them the following instructions:

> The research in which you are participating studies two types of behavior: (1) the effects of self-disclosure on the discussion of current issues; and (2) the behavior of group representatives during a discussion with an opposing representative from a second group. The research session is divided into three phases, which are described in the sheet to be distributed.

2.   Conduct of the Experiment
    a.   Distribute the instruction sheets. Give each pair five minutes to read the sheet and discuss the task between them. Intervene at the end of five minutes and review the entire procedure to determine whether or not the subjects understand what they are to do.
    b.   Have the subjects proceed with Phase I.
    c.   At the end of 10 minutes, terminate the preparation, and review with the pairs what they will be doing in Phase II.
    d.   Have subjects remain in the cubicles or rooms. Escort the confederates to the rooms of the new subjects, and inform confederates enroute which position (favor or oppose) he or she is to take. Confederates should express the following conditions:

C 1 Self-Disclose/Accept
C 2 Self-Disclose/Reject
C 3 Non-Self-Disclose/Accept
C 4 Non-Self-Disclose/Reject

    e.   Begin Phase II by having the subject present his or her position first, after which the confederate should present his or her position.
    f.   Following the presentations, the subject and the confederate should discuss the issue for the duration of the 15 minutes.

g. At the end of Phase II, confederates should return to their original partners and the Postexperimental Opinion Questionnaire should be administered.

h. After completion of the Postexperimental Opinion Questionnaire, naive subjects should be escorted to a debriefing area, in which they are explained the rationale, purposes, procedures, and ethical issues involved in the experiment.

i. While the first group of subjects is being escorted to the debriefing area, the second group of subjects should be escorted to the cubicles and the second experimental session begun. Repeat procedures as utilized with first group.

3. Tabulation of the Data

a. Record the scores on the five scales for each subject in the following form:

	Condition							
	Self-Disclosure				Non-Self-Disclosure			
	Accept		Reject		Accept		Reject	
	S 1	S 2	S 1	S 2	S 1	S 2	S 1	S 2
Trust for Others								
Similar as a Person								
Similiar in Beliefs and Values								
Liking for Others								
Influenced by Others								

b. Calculate the average of the two subjects for each condition, and record as above.

Name _____   Section _____

Date _____   Instructor _____

Results

1. Under which condition did subjects indicate more trust for the confederates?

2. Under which condition was the confederate perceived to be more similar as a person to the subject?

3. Under which condition did the subjects like the confederates more?

4. Under which condition did the subjects feel that the confederates influenced their behavior more?

5. Under which condition did the subjects indicate that the confederates were similiar to them in beliefs and values?

6. What do these results say about the relationships of trust to cooperative interaction and effective interpersonal relationships?

7. Describe the condition in which optimal interpersonal relationships will exist.

Explanation

1. Write a concise summary of this experiment and the results obtained.

2. What conclusions can be drawn from this experiment about self-disclosure, acceptance, and trust?

3. What do the results of this experiment suggest about how to interact with others in order to create the most desirable climate for cooperation?

Script 1: Favor Legalization/Personal

I had the occasion the other day of visiting a state-controlled facility whose purpose was to rehabilitate some of the bad cases of retarded and mongoloid children of the area. The task was obviously futile and frustrating. Worse, it could have been avoided. Medical records indicate that a large percentage of these children could have been identified as high risks to be defective at the early stages of pregnancy. What better justification for terminating the pregnancy than that? Why should we make a child and his parents suffer socially and financially when it could be avoided?

Many extremist groups maintain that abortion is akin to murder. This is totally absurd. A woman should have power over her body and be able to choose what she can and can't do. Until a child is removed from a mother's womb and can exist on its own, is it another person? Murder implies the wanton act of snuffing out another person's life. The courts have even recognized when life begins.

I believe that the legalization of abortions will serve in the public interest. The chance of the tragedy occurring of having a child with a birth defect will be significantly reduced. Children won't have to enter a home unwanted, to be ignored and abused. Further, it will help young mothers delay the responsibility of raising a family.

Murder occurs when the back-street butchers perform illegal abortions. The restrictions on abortions have forced women who should be able to make a responsible decision to chance life itself with incompetent and untrained abortionists. Making abortions available will serve as a necessary stopgap to education on the proper use of contraceptive devices.

What right do we have to subject a human life to misery and frustration? Children who are suffering from birth defects ought to be protected from life— not granted it. Don't be deceived by the disciples of life. Life has meaning if you have a chance to cope with your environment. It becomes a horrible prison for the retarded and the totally crippled. What do you think?

Scripts 1, 2, 3, and 4 were written by Charles Mac Haddow, Brigham Young University.

Script 2: Favor Legalization/Impersonal

One of the basic foundations of this country is the concept of freedom. Human dignity and the right to live as we choose to live includes the right to individualism. Whatever feelings you might have about the increased number of abortions in this country, there are a number of important ideas that must be considered.

First, a woman who chooses to have an abortion generally must make that decision under heavy strain. Presently, the decision must overcome the presumption against its legality imposed by our archaic laws. The choice is further complicated by the high risk involved. Self-inducement or amateur butchering are not good ways to accomplish the goal. Too often there are no choices for the women involved. Abortion is imperative. It seems somewhat barbaric for our society to impose such a fate on thousands of young women every year. Even a casual perusal of medical records shows a startling number of reported injuries and deaths related to illegal abortions attempted.

Second, the legalization of abortion statutes fulfills a vital societal need. Many psychologists have indicated that the mental health of a woman facing an abortion is just as much a concern as her physical health. Forced continuation of an unwanted pregnancy is dangerous to the mother and child. Even the woman who makes her own decision does so to avoid the stigma of becoming a criminal.

It is difficult to assess the true impact that legalization of abortions would have in the numbers of abortions performed. Results in New York indicate that the number of abortions increased slightly in the first year of liberalized abortion statutes and then tapered off. It doesn't seem that legalizing abortions will increase the number of abortions as much as it will provide a safe alternative to illegal abortions.

This is not to suggest that abortions should be taken casually. Abortions should never be used as a mass contraception device. The large number of abortions necessary today is indicative of a deep-rooted medical or social failure. Nonetheless, the benefits accrued are much greater than to continue to uphold so tenuous a principle.

Script 3: Oppose Legalization/Personal

I heard a speaker the other day discuss the need in our society for reevaluation of our values. He said we need to accept some previously unaccepted practices, such as abortions, for the good of society.

Whenever I hear the word "abortion" I get a sick feeling in the pit of my stomach. I cannot understand how a woman who was willing to accept the responsibility of having a sexual relationship would somehow choose to abdicate the greater responsibility of the consequences of the act. The truth of the matter is that abortion is just a fancy way of saying murder. This isn't the same kind of murder we see on television when the crook murders a policeman. At least the victim could have escaped his demise by using equal force, running away, or dodging the attacker. No, this kind of murder is an even greater sin. It is the brutal snuffing of an innocent baby's life who stands utterly defenseless. The child cannot escape his fate by using force because he has no tools to do so; he cannot run away or dodge his attacker because his home becomes a prison. The mother's womb becomes a death chamber more horrible than any contrived by man.

I cannot imagine any greater travesty to society than to permit the wholesale abortion of human lives. We give the choice of life and death to a mother over her child. We don't allow the child to make his own decision about living or dying, let alone just breathing, eating, or sleeping. What cancer is it that has attached itself to this society that permits the thought to be viewed by many as valid and necessary?

Some people claim that abortions are justified if the child is unwanted. Let the mother release the child then. There are thousands of couples who cannot bear children who would give all the love necessary. We don't suffer from a lack of love in this society, just from an unjustified importance attached to those who have no love to give.

Don't be deceived by the disciples of the devil who advocate the legalization of this ominous practice. Abortion is murder—pure and simple. What forgiveness can be given to such people? What measure of mercy? None. None whatsoever.

Script 4: Oppose Legalization/Impersonal

Theodore Spencer, in the play *An Act of Life,* wrote that "the eunuchs, abortive platonists and priests, speak always very wisely about love." Our culture produces its own brand of pseudo-intelligent experts who always speak very wisely about love and abortions. The rate of abortions is increasing at an alarming rate in our nation, largely due to the permissive ruling of the U.S. Supreme Court.

There is no legal justification for granting the power of life and death to one person over another. The Supreme Court ignored the biological evidence of the attributes of life that unborn children have from the first movement of conception. In doing so, we deny the right of personhood or citizenship to all those who are lost to abortions.

Regardless of the implications of destroying the life of an innocent baby, abortions encourage irresponsibility among young people. Wanton acts don't bear the same consequences. Many say that the children are better off than being born into a home unwanted. Perhaps so, but the alternatives seem diverse enough to make abortions an extreme solution. Life is a divine gift that cannot be willed away at a moment's notice. Rather it is a gift to be prized and protected. Children with birth defects generally have a capacity to love and all of them have the potential to be loved. That's different from our society's eunuchs, abortive platonists, and priests speaking always wisely about love.

Briefing Sheet

These arguments have been listed in order to facilitate your preparation of a group defense. Your group may develop other arguments that support your position.

Issue: Abortion should be illegal in this country.

Arguments that *support* this statement:

1.   The fetus is a human life; life is present at conception; you can't take a chance by guessing when human life begins.

2.   Abortion is murder. No one but God has the right to take a life.

3.   An unborn child has more right to live than a woman who has experienced life.

4.   An abortion doesn't solve the real problem of an inability to give love and accept responsibility without qualification. Psychological rather than medical treatment is required.

Briefing Sheet

These arguments have been listed in order to facilitate your preparation of a group defense. Your group may develop other arguments that support your position.

Issue: Abortion should be illegal in this country.

Arguments that *oppose* this statement:

1.   A woman has the right to determine whether or not she wants a child.

2.   The fetus is not a human life but merely potentially human.

3.   The abortion laws do not work. Women who want to terminate a pregnancy will do so despite the law.

4.   The world is already overpopulated. It is senseless to bring more unwanted children into the world.

Instruction Sheet for Research Sessions

Phase I

Your group has 10 minutes to prepare one another for the meeting with a representative from the opposing position. Research has shown that individuals who use their own feelings and experiences in discussion with others are more likely to make them understand their position more clearly. An opinion about the issue of abortion usually involves emotional as well as factual material. In your discussion with the person from the opposing position (Phase II), we would like you to take a *personal* approach, disclosing your *feelings* about the issue and what in your background led to the development of your feelings and attitudes. Try to find arguments that can be supported by your *personal feelings and experiences.*

It is sometimes difficult to discuss issues with a stranger in a very personal way. *This experiment, though, depends on your willingness to do this. Your cooperation is extremely important.*

Phase I has been designed to help you prepare for this discussion. You and your partner should:

1. Prepare a presentation based on your feelings and experiences.
2. Practice expressing your position with each other.

Some suggestions for effectively disclosing your feelings are:

1. Try to begin statements with phrases such as "I feel," "It's important to me," and so on.
2. Try to support any argument with a statement of personal feeling or an example from your own experience.
3. Express your position in terms of application to your own life.

The briefing sheet has been organized to facilitiate your preparation.

Phase II

In this phase, lasting approximately 15 minutes, you will meet with a representative from the opposing group; that is, each of you will meet with one other person who holds an opposing opinion. The meeting will consist of the following procedure:

1. The representative from each side will present his or her position. The individual who presents first will be chosen randomly.
2. After each side has presented his or her position, you will have ten minutes for free discussion, during which you should try to arrive at a mutual understanding.
3. The representatives from the opposing groups will be separated; the specific procedure will be explained by the experimenter.

Phase III

During this phase you will meet with your partner to review the discussion and to report the outcome of the meeting with the representative from the opposing group.

Postexperimental Opinion Questionnaire

Instructions: Please check one:

☐ I favor legalizing abortion.

☐ I oppose legalizing abortion.

Postexperimental Attitude Scales

Instructions: Please check the number that best represents your attitude on each of the scales at this moment for each question asked.

1. To what extent do you trust the representative from the other group?

    Great Deal ___ : ___ : ___ : ___ : ___ : ___ : ___ Very Little
    　　　　　　　1　　2　　3　　4　　5　　6　　7

2. To what extent do you perceive the representative from the other group to be similar to you as a person?

    Great Deal ___ : ___ : ___ : ___ : ___ : ___ : ___ Very Little
    　　　　　　　1　　2　　3　　4　　5　　6　　7

3. To what extent do you perceive the representative from the other group to be similar to you in beliefs and values?

    Great Deal ___ : ___ : ___ : ___ : ___ : ___ : ___ Very Little
    　　　　　　　1　　2　　3　　4　　5　　6　　7

4. To what extent do you like the representative from the other group?

    Great Deal ___ : ___ : ___ : ___ : ___ : ___ : ___ Very Little
    　　　　　　　1　　2　　3　　4　　5　　6　　7

5. To what extent did the opinions of the representative from the other group influence your behavior?

    Great Deal ___ : ___ : ___ : ___ : ___ : ___ : ___ Very Little
    　　　　　　　1　　2　　3　　4　　5　　6　　7

Experiment 2.2
Relevant Responses

Proposition
Interpersonal relationships tend to improve when both parties communicate a warm, positive understanding of each other by giving relevant responses.

Research Questions
Does accurately restating the content and feelings of a person's conversation increase understanding?

Are people more willing to negotiate when compromises are proposed than when they are not?

Do expressions of warmth lead to more favorable attitudes toward individuals involved in interaction?

Research Methods*

Subjects
Eight naive subjects who are not members of this class.

Four confederates who are informed class members.

Materials
Role Descriptions for Experimental Conditions (Informed Confederates) (4 copies).

Case Description for Confederates: Meekers vs. Bear Mountain Inn (4 copies for Confederates only).

Case Description for Naive Subjects: Meekers vs. Bear Mountain Club (4 copies).

Instruction Sheet for Research Sessions (12 copies).

Questionnaire 1 (12 copies).

Questionnaire 2 (12 copies).

Phase III Report Form (12 copies).

Tokens or some other reward.

Four stopwatches or clocks with sweep second hands.

Procedures
1. Selection and Preparation of Subjects
    a. Orientation and Training of Confederates
        (1) Confederates should be trained to exhibit the appropriate behavior as described in the Role Description sheet and guided through several pilot interviews with subjects before the experiment begins.

*Adapted from an experiment reported in David W. Johnson, "Effects of Warmth of Interaction, Accuracy of Understanding, and the Proposal of Compromises on Listener's Behavior," *Journal of Counseling Psychology,* Vol. 18 (1971), pp. 207-216. By permission.

(2) During Phase II negotiations, confederates will represent the Meekers and seek a settlement; distribute copies of the Meekers vs. Bear Mountain Inn case for confederates to study in advance.

(3) Assign each confederate to one of the following experimental conditions:

C 1 Compromise/Warm/Accurate
C 2 Compromise/Warm/Inaccurate
C 3 Compromise/Cold/Accurate
C 4 Compromise/Cold/Inaccurate

With the second set of naive subjects, the order of the conditions will be the same, except no compromises will be offered.

b. Ask the eight naive subjects to arrive at the experimental area at an appointed time. Select four subjects for the first trial; escort the other four subjects to a lounge until the second trial.

2. Conduct of the Experiment

a. Have two large cubicles or separate rooms in which a group of four subjects can meet.

b. Place the subjects in groups of four, consisting of two confederates and two naive subjects, and have them go to their separate areas.

c. Explain to both groups that they are competing against a similar group of four meeting in a different room. Give each group a description of a hypothetical court case about a civil law suit (Bear Mountain Club case).

d. Distribute copies of the Instruction Sheet for Research Sessions, and ask the group members to read the instructions. After about 5 minutes, intervene and determine whether any misunderstandings concerning objectives and procedures persist. Have subjects proceed with Phase I.

e. At the end of 15 minutes, terminate the preparation and administer Questionnaire 1.

f. Collect Questionnaire 1, and review procedures for Phase II. Escort *confederates* to the meeting area of the other group; pair confederates with naive subjects for negotiations. It is desirable to have four separate meeting rooms or cubicles that provide for minimum interference during negotiations.

How to Pair Ss and Cs

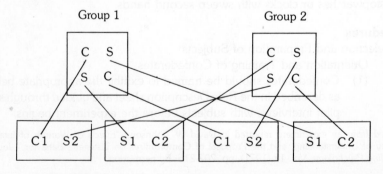

46

g. Begin Phase II with the confederate, now representing the Meekers, presenting his or her position first. Next, give the subject representing the Bear Mountain Club 5 minutes to present his or her position. At that point, devote 15 minutes to open discussion, in which the confederate implements the experimental conditions.

h. At the end of an agreement or the 15-minute period, confederates return to their original groups. Subjects then complete Questionnaire 2 and the Phase III Report Form.

i. While the first group of subjects is being escorted out of the experimental area, the second group should be escorted in, and the procedures should be repeated under the no-compromise conditions.

3. Tabulation of the Data

a. Tally the responses of each subject to Questionnaire 1.

	Subjects							
	Compromise				No Compromise			
Item	1	2	3	4	1	2	3	4
1. Satisfied								
2. Same Group								
3. Money								
4. Task								
5. Groups Compare Similar								
Compatible								
Superior								
6. Feelings								

b. Record the scores on Questionnaire 2 for attitude scale items 3–26, for each condition and each subject on the following form:

Scale	Compromise				No Compromise			
	Warm		Cold		Warm		Cold	
	Accur	Inacc	Accur	Inacc	Accur	Inacc	Accur	Inacc
3								
4								
5								
6								
7								
8								
9								
10								
11								
12								
13								
14								
15								
16								
17								
18								
19								
20								
21								
22								
23								
24								
25								
26								

Part 1   Experiments about Relationships

c. Tally the number of subjects in each condition who did and did not reach agreement, how many minutes it took to reach an agreement, and the amount of money the Meekers should receive from the Bear Mountain Club (see Phase III Report Form).

| | Compromise | | | | No Compromise | | | |
| | Warm | | Cold | | Warm | | Cold | |
	Accur	Inacc	Accur	Inacc	Accur	Inacc	Accur	Inacc
Reached Agreement								
No Agreement								
Amount of Money to Meekers: 0								
250								
500								
750								
1,000								
1,250								
1,500								
Minutes: 0–2								
2–5								
5–10								
10–15								

Name _____   Section _____

Date _____   Instructor _____

Results

1.   Under which condition was the largest number of agreements reached?

2.   Under which condition did the subject feel that the confederate was most understanding?

3.   Under which condition did the subjects see the confederates as agreeing with their position more?

4.   Under which condition was the confederate perceived as more willing to compromise?

5.   Under which condition did the subjects privately feel that the Meekers should receive more money?

6.   Under which condition did the subjects trust the confederate most?

7.   Under which condition did the subjects perceive their relationship with the confederates as more cooperative?

8.   Under which condition did the confederate attempt to understand the subject's position more?

9.   Under which condition was the confederate viewed as a more understanding person?

10.   Under which condition did the subject feel that the confederate agreed with him or her more?

11.   Under which condition did the subject feel that the confederate was more accepting of the subject's position?

12.   Under which condition did the subject feel more willing to compromise?

13.   Under which condition did the subject feel that his or her position was superior to that of the Meekers?

Explanation

1.   Write a concise summary of this experiment and the results obtained.

2.   What factors seem to increase perceived trustworthiness?

3.   If accurate understanding produces attitude change only in subjects in cold conditions, what are the implications for being warm and accurate at the same time?

4.   In what ways is warmth related to being liked and trusted?

5.   How are attraction, perceived similarity, and warmth of interaction related to reaching an agreement?

6.   How does proposing compromises affect perceptions of agreement between the two parties?

7.   If you want to reach an agreement, are you better off proposing compromises or not? Why?

Role Descriptions for Experimental Conditions (Informed Confederates)

Warmth
Feelings are communicated through tone of voice, facial expressions, eye contact, and posture. Confederates should be trained to have a warm vocal tone, lean toward the subject, and look into the subject's eyes.

Coldness
Confederates should have a cold tone of voice, lean away from the subject, and avoid looking into the subject's eyes.

Accuracy of Understanding
Confederates should reflect back the content and feelings of the subject's position by giving a complete and accurate restatement of it.

Inaccurate Understanding
Confederates should reflect back an inaccurate and incomplete restatement of the subject's position.

Compromises
In attempting to reach agreement on how much money Mr. and Mrs. Meeker should receive from the Bear Mountain Club, the possible amount varies between zero (the BMC position) to $1,500 (the Meekers' position). During negotiations, confederates should accept at any time a $750 settlement if one is proposed by the subject even in the no-compromise condition. In conditions where the confederates propose compromises, they should propose that the Meekers receive $1,500 until there is 10 minutes of negotiating time left, $1,250 until there is 5 minutes of negotiating time left, $1,000 until there is 1 minute left, and $750 until the time ends.

Case Description for Confederates:
Meekers vs. Bear Mountain Inn

Twenty years ago, Mr. and Mrs. Philip Meeker were married. During their honeymoon they stayed at the Bear Mountain Inn, a well-known summer resort in New York. For their 20th anniversary, the Meekers returned to the inn. On June 4, 1963, they stopped and asked directions from a local citizen as to how they could find the Bear Mountain Inn. The man gave them directions, and they proceeded to the inn. The lobby was empty, but a young man appeared behind the desk through a door marked employees only. The Meekers requested their old room and were told it was occupied, but that it would be free about 6 o'clock. It was then about 4 o'clock. Mrs. Meeker checked some jewelry she didn't wish to carry: a diamond bar-pin worth $600, a platinum bracelet worth $500, and $400 in cash. The man handed Mrs. Meeker a receipt and told her he'd place the valuables in the safe. At 6 o'clock, a different man was behind the desk. He claimed to know nothing of the jewels or the other man. When called, the manager seemed surprised at Mr. Meeker's questions about the room and asked if the Meekers knew this was a club, not a hotel, and not open to the public. Neither the valuables nor the young man could be found. The manager disclaimed all responsibility, and the Meekers sued.

The Meekers claim the Bear Mountain Club continued to operate as a hotel and is therefore liable for their loss. The relevant law states that if an establishment operates as a hotel or appears to the public as such, then it owes the people on its property a duty of care; that is, it is responsible for them and their property. In court it was brought out that most people still considered the establishment to be an inn. Two witnesses testified to this fact. Frank Fleharty, who is not a member of the club and does not have a guest card, stated that he stays at the inn every summer from three to four weeks, and some of his friends do the same. James Thompson, who lives in the area of the Bear Mountain Inn, stated that all the local residents call the establishment an inn, that local people still eat there regularly, and that many out-of-towners stay there without having a membership card or a guest card.

The Meekers stated in court that the signs stating the establishment is a private club are inconspicuous and, therefore, not seriously intended to keep people from thinking it is an inn. They submitted as evidence a picture showing a small sign half-hidden by bushes near the entrance and a picture showing a second sign over the desk which has to do with restrictions to people with membership cards or members only, inconspicuously hanging among the trophies on the wall. They also submitted as evidence the receipt they were given for their valuables.

It is your position that the Bear Mountain Club owes the Meekers $1,500, as they are responsible for the loss of the Meekers' jewelry and money. They operate as a hotel, they appear to the public to be a hotel, and, therefore, they owe anyone who comes upon their grounds a duty of care.

Case Description for Naive Subjects:
Meekers vs. Bear Mountain Club

On June 4, 1963, the Bear Mountain Club was holding its annual golf tournament. All club personnel were on the golf course assisting with the tournament.

Mr. Richard Howard, the club clerk, returned to his desk at about 5 o'clock in the afternoon. At 6 o'clock a Mr. and Mrs. Meeker came in with a receipt made out by a man Mr. Howard had never heard of. The Meekers claimed to have checked jewelry and cash at 4 o'clock. Informing the Meekers he knew nothing of their valuables, Mr. Howard explained how 5 years ago a private club was made out of the Bear Mountain Inn. The manager, Mr. Thomas Wheeler, was called. Mr. Wheeler also looked carefully for the valuables and explained that the establishment was not open to the public. The Meekers left outraged. A careful search failed to turn up the valuables, and Mr. Wheeler wrote the Meekers to that effect.

Upon receiving the letter, the Meekers sued the Bear Mountain Club for $1,500, the value of the jewelry and money they stated they lost there. The grounds of the suit were that the Bear Mountain Club was operating as a hotel and therefore was responsible for their loss. The relevant law states that if an establishment operates as a hotel or appears to the public to be a hotel, then it owes the people on its grounds a duty of care; that is, it is responsible for them and their property.

In court, Mr. Howard testified that the club is for members only. Each guest is given a guest card. People without memberships or guest cards are asked to leave. He stated that he has never taken valuables from the guests since there are lockers which are rented for that purpose. There is no place for him to keep valuables.

Mr. Thomas Wheeler, the manager, testified that when the Meekers demanded that he make their loss good, he told them that the club was not liable because it was a club, not an inn. Calling the signs to the Meekers' attention, Mr. Wheeler said the Meekers did not remember seeing the signs and were not sure who they had given their valuables to. The fact that the clerk was not at the desk was not unusual; both he and the clerk knew all the members by sight, so there never had been any trouble with the members. It was very improbable that an outsider could get a room at the club without a guest card. As for the signs, Mr. Wheeler stated that one was a huge sign which hung over the entrance to the driveway. The letters are 2½ feet high. The second is a sign which hangs over the desk in the main lobby.

Mr. Samuel Hummel, one of the owners of the club, also testified. He stated that the club had done everything possible to make people stop thinking the club was an inn and to make the public stop coming there. One example is the two signs stating Bear Mountain is a private club. It is the duty of the clerk to see that no one is allowed in besides the members and their guests, and the clerk does his job well. There are lockers in the club which members may rent, although the club assumes no responsibility for the contents. A few friends are allowed to come and stay at the club even though they are not members. Frank Fleharty is an example.

It is your position that the Bear Mountain Club does not owe the Meekers $1,500 since it does *not* operate as a hotel and does *not* appear to the public to be a hotel. The Club, therefore, does not owe the people who wander on its grounds a duty of care.

Instruction Sheet for Research Sessions

The research in which you are to participate studies three types of behaviors: (1) the group planning of a common position, (2) the behavior of group representatives who meet with an opposing representative from a second group, and (3) the group evaluation of the agreements made by each member in the meeting with the other representative. The research session is divided into three corresponding phases, which are outlined below.

Phase I

Your group has 15 minutes to develop a group defense for the Bear Mountain Club in the court case you see in front of you. The court case is entitled "Meekers vs. Bear Mountain Club" and is a record of a civil law suit. The other group has a different description, which represents a directly opposing point of view concerning the court case. Read the court case carefully, and prepare yourself and the other members of your group as well as possible for the meeting with the opposing group. This can be done by: (1) summarizing the most important points in the case description, (2) arriving at any new arguments you can for the position of your group, and (3) giving each other any feelings or advice you have about the meeting with the opposing representatives.

Phase II

In this phase you will meet with a representative from the opposing group. The meeting will consist of the following procedure:

1. The representative from each group will have up to 5 minutes to present his or her group's position.
2. There will be 15 minutes in which to develop a joint solution to the court case. This will be a free discussion; that is, you may proceed in any way you like.

Your challenge and reward depends upon: (1) how quickly you reach a joint agreement and (2) how close the agreement is to your original group position (if there is a joint agreement). Each member of your group will receive zero tokens if no agreement is reached, but 100 tokens if a joint agreement is reached. Second, your group will receive up to 100 additional tokens, depending upon how close the joint agreement is to the original position of your group (if a joint agreement is reached). Thus, it is possible for each member of your group to get from zero (if he and the representative from the other group do not reach an agreement) to 200 tokens for your group (if he and the representative from the other group reach an agreement which is most favorable to your group); the group, therefore, can receive between zero and 800 tokens.

Each of you will meet with an opposing representative from the other group. During this meeting, your task is to gain as many tokens as you can for your group. You have no interest whatsoever in whether the other group wins or loses. This is *not* a competitive situation, but neither are you out to help the other group. You simply want to gain as many tokens for your group as you can.

Over

Phase III

During this phase you will meet with your group to report on the joint agreement (if any) that you reached with your opponent.

Name_____ Condition_____ Subject No. ____

Questionnaire 1

1. How satisfied are you with your group's position?

Very Satisfied ___ : ___ : ___ : ___ : ___ : ___ : ___ Very Dissatisfied
              1   2   3   4   5   6   7

2. If you were to take part in this experiment again, and had the choice of being a member of this group or of another group with different people, would you want to participate with this group again?

Definitely Yes ___ : ___ : ___ : ___ : ___ : ___ : ___ Definitely No
            1   2   3   4   5   6   7

3. At this point, how much money do you think the Meekers should receive from the Bear Mountain Club? The Meekers should receive (circle one):

$$\$0 \quad 250 \quad 500 \quad 750 \quad 1,000 \quad 1,250 \quad 1,500$$

4. How do you see your task in the meeting with the representative from the other group? (Check one.)

_____ For your group to make more money than the other group.

_____ To gain as much money as possible for your group, regardless of how much the other group makes.

5. On the basis of your expectations, how do you think your group's position compares with the position of the other group? Answer as best you can.

Very Similar ___ : ___ : ___ : ___ : ___ : ___ : ___ Very Different
            1   2   3   4   5   6   7

Very Compatible ___ : ___ : ___ : ___ : ___ : ___ : ___ Very Incompatible
            1   2   3   4   5   6   7

My Group's Position Is Superior ___ : ___ : ___ : ___ : ___ : ___ : ___ My Group's Position Is Inferior
            1   2   3   4   5   6   7

6. Very briefly, at this point, how do you feel about yourself, your group, the other group, and the activities in general?

Questionnaire 2

Included in this questionnaire are several questions dealing with your reactions to the behavior of the representative from the other group. You may be acquainted with the representative from the other group; but in filling out this questionnaire, please respond to the questions *only* on the basis of how you would have reacted to the person if he or she had been a complete stranger. That is, disregard everything but his behavior in the negotiations, and complete the questionnaire *as if* the representative from the other group were a complete stranger to you at the beginning of Phase 2.

1. What do you think the experiment was about?

2. What do you think the experiment measures?

3. To what extent did the representative from the other group attempt to understand your group's position?

Great Deal ___ : ___ : ___ : ___ : ___ : ___ : ___ Very Little
           1   2   3   4   5   6   7

4. How similar as a person are you and the representative from the other group?

Very Similar ___ : ___ : ___ : ___ : ___ : ___ : ___ Very Dissimilar
           1   2   3   4   5   6   7

5. How similar in beliefs and values are you and the representative from the other group?

Very Similar ___ : ___ : ___ : ___ : ___ : ___ : ___ Very Dissimilar
           1   2   3   4   5   6   7

6. How much do you like the representative from the other group?

Great Deal ___ : ___ : ___ : ___ : ___ : ___ : ___ Very Little
           1   2   3   4   5   6   7

7. How satisfied are you with your performance in negotiations?

Great Deal ___ : ___ : ___ : ___ : ___ : ___ : ___ Very Little
           1   2   3   4   5   6   7

8. How satisfied are you with the task assigned to you?

Great Deal ___ : ___ : ___ : ___ : ___ : ___ : ___ Very Little
           1   2   3   4   5   6   7

9.   At this point, what is your private opinion about how much money the Meekers should receive from the Bear Mountain Club? The Meekers should receive:

$$\$0 \quad 250 \quad 500 \quad 750 \quad 1,000 \quad 1,250 \quad 1,500$$

10.   To what extent were you willing to compromise during the negotiations with the representative from the other group?

Great Deal ___ : ___ : ___ : ___ : ___ : ___ : ___ Very Little
                1   2   3   4   5   6   7

11.   To what extent was the representative from the other group willing to compromise during the negotiations?

Great Deal ___ : ___ : ___ : ___ : ___ : ___ : ___ Very Little
                1   2   3   4   5   6   7

12.   Did you change your opinion about the amount of money the Meekers should receive during the negotiations?

___ Yes   ___ No

13.   To what extent do you trust the representative from the other group?

Great Deal ___ : ___ : ___ : ___ : ___ : ___ : ___ Very Little
                1   2   3   4   5   6   7

14.   If you had proposed a compromise to the representative from the other group, how likely was it that he would accept or propose a countercompromise?

Very Likely ___ : ___ : ___ : ___ : ___ : ___ : ___ Very Unlikely
                 1   2   3   4   5   6   7

15.   Were you willing to compromise during the negotiations?

___ Yes   ___ No

If yes, why? If no, why not?

16.   How accurately did the representative from the other group understand your group's position?

Highly Accurate ___ : ___ : ___ : ___ : ___ : ___ : ___ Highly Inaccurate
                      1   2   3   4   5   6   7

17.   Would there have been any difference in outcome if you had been willing to compromise?

___ Better off compromising   ___ Better off not compromising

18. How accepting of you as a person was the person who represented the Meekers?

Highly Accepting ___ : ___ : ___ : ___ : ___ : ___ : ___ Highly Rejecting
                   1   2   3   4   5   6   7

19. How accepting was the person who represented the Meekers of your position of representing the Bear Mountain Club?

Highly Accepting ___ : ___ : ___ : ___ : ___ : ___ : ___ Highly Rejecting
                   1   2   3   4   5   6   7

20. To what extent did the person representing the Meekers communicate warmth toward you as a person?

Very Warm ___ : ___ : ___ : ___ : ___ : ___ : ___ Very Cool
            1   2   3   4   5   6   7

21. How understanding, as a person, was the person who represented the Meekers?

Very   Very Non-
Understanding ___ : ___ : ___ : ___ : ___ : ___ : ___ understanding
                1   2   3   4   5   6   7

22. Which position do you think is superior?

___ Meekers   ___ Bear Mountain Club

23. If you participated in this experiment again, which position would you rather represent?

___ Meekers   ___ Bear Mountain Club

24. How would you describe your relationship with the person who represents the Meekers?

Cooperative ___ : ___ : ___ : ___ : ___ : ___ : ___ Competitive
              1   2   3   4   5   6   7

25. To what extent does the other person agree with your position?

Completely   Completely
Agree   ___ : ___ : ___ : ___ : ___ : ___ : ___ Disagree
             1   2   3   4   5   6   7

26. To what extent do you agree with the other person's position?

Completely   Completely
Agree   ___ : ___ : ___ : ___ : ___ : ___ : ___ Disagree
             1   2   3   4   5   6   7

Name_____ Condition_____ Subject No. _____

Phase III Report Form

1. Did you and the representative from the other group reach an agreement?

    _____ Yes   _____ No

2. If *yes,* how many minutes did it take to reach an agreement?

    If *yes,* indicate the nature of the agreement.

3. If *no*—that is, you have not reached an agreement—indicate the extent to which you would have been willing to concede in order to reach an agreement on the amount of money the Meekers should receive from the Bear Mountain Club (circle one):

    $0   250   500   750   1,000   1,250   1,500

Part 2
Experiments about Messages

Chapter 3
Message Reception and Processing

Human beings share information and develop common understanding through the processes of message reception and processing. Anything that can be interpreted by another human being can be considered a message. An axiom of communication theory states that a person cannot *not* communicate. That means, of course, that by existing, you serve as a potential source of something to be interpreted—a message. Thus, anytime you interact with another person, *you* are a message, *what* you say is a message, *how* you say it is a message, and *where* you say it may be still another message. The way in which a person interacts, misinterprets, understands, and creates meaning out of the available messages is what we refer to as *message reception* and *processing*.

Experiments on message reception and processing have been conducted in diversified subject areas. Those that follow provide only a sketchy introduction to the methods and procedures utilized to learn about how people create meaning. Nevertheless, what we do know about these processes is derived from such experiments. Compare the results against your own experience.

Experiment 3.1
Selective Perception

Proposition

Messages tend to be selectively perceived and processed.

Research Questions

To what degree is an eyewitness to a spontaneous event able to report accurately what occurred?

What kinds of information are reported most accurately and what kinds most inaccurately?

Research Methods*

Subjects

A class of at least 75 students in which a discussion of factors that influence perception would not be out of place.

Four confederate students from that class.

Materials

Two silver dollars or equivalent size metal discs.

One copy of the textbook used in that class.

Procedures

1. Selection and Preparation of Subjects
    a. Arrange with an instructor to use an appropriate class at a time when a short explanation and demonstration of influences on perception can be given.
    b. Select four students from the class and the instructor, and give them the following directions:

    Instructor—During the period prior to the experiment, assign the class a brief report on "An Accident I Have Observed Recently" that will be turned in the day of the experiment.

    Confederate A—As the instructor begins to collect the reports from the front row, A should hit B with his fist.

    Confederate B—Upon being hit, B should retaliate by hitting A with the textbook.

    Confederate C—As B is striking A with the book, throw the two silver dollars or discs into the air, permit them to fall to the floor, scramble after them, and then pick them up.

    Confederate D—As the instructor orders confederates A, B, and C to leave the room, D should get up and walk out of the room.

2. Conduct of the Experiment
    a. Have the confederates sit in the classroom according to the diagram at the top of page 69.
    b. The instructor should begin the class period with an explanation of a visual illusion, such as the Mueller-Lyer figure. Introduce the figure, but then pause and announce that you would like to gather the reports due for this day. Proceed to the front row and begin collecting the reports.

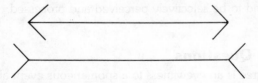

*Adapted from an experiment reported in M. C. Otto, "Testimony and Human Nature," *Journal of Criminal Law and Criminology,* Vol. 9 (1919), pp. 98–104. By special permission of the Journal of Criminal Law and Criminology, Copyright © 1919 by Northwestern University School of Law.

Exit   Blackboard

                          Instructor
                                            Confed.
                                              C
            Confed.
              D

                                                              Exit

                                              Confed. Confed.
                                                 A   B

c. After the instructor has collected about four papers, confederate A should hit B with his fist, and B should retaliate by striking A with his textbook; the two should begin to quarrel very loudly.

d. The instructor should stop short of C and call to A and B; at that moment, C should throw the two discs into the air and retrieve them from the floor as quickly as possible.

e. The instructor should order A, B, and C to leave the room; as they leave, D should stand up and walk normally out of the room by the nearest exit.

f. As the confederates are preparing to leave, the instructor should walk to the blackboard, glance at his watch, write the time on the blackboard, erase it, and write it again.

g. As soon as the confederates have left, the instructor should turn to the class and say, in effect: "You have all seen what has happened. I must report this incident to the department chairman, and I may very well call upon you to give testimony. Please take a few minutes to write up a report of what you observed." Allow no discussion of the incident until the reports have been collected.

h. To give order to the reports, the instructor and the class should agree to include answers to the following questions:
   (1) Where was the instructor when the disturbance began?
   (2) Where was the instructor and what was he doing when the confederates left the room?
   (3) What did C do?
   (4) How did A, B, and C look as they left the room?
   (5) How did the disturbance begin?
   (6) (Add other questions that the class feels are relevant.)
   i. Allow students time to write their reports; then collect them, call in the confederates, and debrief the class; indicate that the reports will be analyzed and the information discussed at a later meeting. Continue with the class.
3. Tabulation of the Data
   a. Tally the answers to each of the above questions given by each student (subject).

Subject	Question					
	1	2	3	4	5	6
1						
2						
3						
4						
5						
6						
7						
8						
9						

Continue this tally on additional paper so that each subject who submitted a report is accounted for.

   b. Make a list of items appearing in the reports that are not a part of the basic questions. Use a separate sheet of paper for this tabulation.

Name _____   Section _____

Date _____   Instructor _____

Results

1. How many students answered the basic questions accurately?

	Question					
	1	2	3	4	5	6
Answering Correctly						
Answering Incorrectly						
Answering Don't Know						

2. What did the reports reveal about the accuracy with which so-called eyewitnesses observe and describe incidents?

3. What factors seem to account for the general reliability of the eyewitness reports?

4. What kinds of information seemed to be reported most accurately?

5. In your opinion, were the reports given here any more or any less accurate than those generally given by eyewitnesses of accidents, crimes, or other incidents?

Explanation

1. Write a concise summary of this experiment and the results obtained.

2. What conclusions can be drawn from this study about how eyewitnesses perceive and report incidents that they observe?

Experiment 3.2
Organization and Retention

Proposition
Message retention is usually enhanced when messages are adequately organized.

Research Questions
Do subjects who hear an adequately organized speech tend to retain more than subjects who hear a grossly disorganized speech?

Does a person's ability in organization influence how much is retained from a more versus a less adequately organized speech?

Research Methods*

Subjects
Forty individuals divided into two groups of 20 each by means of scores on a test of organization ability.

Materials
Goyer Organization of Ideas Test for each subject (40 copies).†

A ten-minute taped speech: Adequately Organized Speech.

A ten-minute taped speech: Grossly Disorganized Speech.

Tape recorder for playing the speeches.

Multiple-choice Retention Test for each subject (40 copies).

Procedures
1. Selection and Preparation of Subjects
   a. Administer the *Goyer Organization of Ideas Test* to a fairly large number of subjects, as many as 500 to 600 but not fewer than 60.
   b. Score the tests and select 20 to 30 individuals who scored in the upper third of the distribution and 20 to 30 who scored in the lower third. The sample for the actual experiment will consist of Group 1 (10 upper and 10 lower scorers) and Group 2 (10 lower and 10 upper scorers).
2. Conduct of the Experiment
   a. Play the adequately organized speech to Group 1 (10 high and 10 low scorers). Play the grossly disorganized speech to Group 2 (10 low and 10 high scorers). You may play the respective speeches in the same location on two different days or on the same day in the same location but with an

*Adapted from an experiment reported in Ernest Thompson, "An Experimental Investigation of the Relative Effectiveness of Organizational Structure in Oral Communication," *Southern Speech Journal*, Vol. 26 (Fall 1960), pp. 59–69. By permission.

†Copies of this test will be supplied by your instructor, or you may order copies from Dr. Robert S. Goyer, Director, Center for Communication Studies, Ohio University, Athens, Ohio 45701.

interval of about 20 minutes; or you may play them simultaneously in two different locations.

   b. Immediately following exposure to the speech, administer the multiple-choice Retention Test to each subject in each group.
   c. Collect all materials and debrief subjects.
3. Tabulation of the Data
   a. Score the retention tests, and record the scores for each subject according to each of the four conditions: high organization ability–adequately organized speech; low organization ability–adequately organized speech; high organization ability–grossly disorganized speech; low organization ability–grossly disorganized speech.

Subject	Speech	
	Adequate Organization	Inadequate Organization
High Ability 1		
2		
3		
4		
5		
6		
7		
8		
9		
10		
Low Ability 1		
2		
3		
4		
5		
6		
7		
8		
9		
10		

Part 2   Experiments about Messages

b. Calculate the mean scores for each subgroup on the Retention Test.

Subject Ability	Speech Organization	
	Adequate	Inadequate
High		
Low		

Name _____   Section _____

Date _____   Instructor _____

Results

1. Which group scored the highest on the Retention Test, and which group scored the lowest?

2. Do the results of this study support the hypothesis that the more ability a person has in organization skills, the higher will be his or her retention of the content of a speech?

3. Do more adequately organized speeches seem to result in greater retention?

4. Does the combination of organization ability and an adequately organized speech lead to greater recall at a later time? Does this study answer this question? What would be the appropriate steps to take to get a more satisfactory answer?

Explanation

1. Write a concise summary of this experiment and the results obtained.

2. How do the results of this study answer the research questions?

Adequately Organized Speech

In the year 1914, Henry Ford surprised his competitors, and his employees, by raising the minimum wages of his factory workers from $2.34 a day to $5.00 a day. This was one of the first real gains to be made by the laboring man. As you know, wages have continued to rise—right up to the present time.

In 1955, Henry Ford II agreed, in principle, to a guaranteed annual wage for Ford Company employees. This meant that each employee could be sure of at least a minimum income during the year regardless of how many days he worked. Of course, the more he worked the more he would earn, but he could count on a minimum income even if he were laid off temporarily.

Other companies in the automobile industry followed Ford's lead in this. General Motors almost immediately adopted the same policy as Ford. Other major auto manufacturers did the same. So already a guaranteed annual wage has been introduced into our society.

It is my purpose to discuss with you some aspects of the guaranteed annual wage and to urge your support of it.

The need for such a measure as the guaranteed annual wage is based on the one real weakness of our economy—unemployment. Let's take a look at unemployment in recent years. In 1931–1932, 18 million people were unemployed. In 1939, 9 million people were still unemployed. In 1950, a relatively prosperous year, 4½ million people were unemployed. Even in 1957, unemployment was one of our most pressing national problems. All in all, if we average unemployment during the peacetime years between 1900 and 1950, we find that an average of 8.4% of our working forces was unemployed. Obviously, unemployment is a real problem. A means must be found to combat it, and a guaranteed annual wage will do just that.

It is important to add that the guaranteed annual wage program is a fair and just method of attacking unemployment. It isn't just the working man who suffers when he's unemployed. No doubt he is the hardest hit. We find, for instance, that the typical working man has no savings to fall back on. He is immediately faced with the problem of survival. But it is the grocer, the landlord, and the professional men who must bear the brunt of unpaid bills. Eventually all of us are affected.

One great effect is on industry, itself. When money is short, the consumer can't buy. Laboring men are consumers; so are the unpaid grocers and landlords. Industrial production and profits must necessarily go down. So, it is to industry's advantage to attack the problem of unemployment, and to our advantage to support such a program.

Industry has already recognized its responsibility in this matter of unemployment. The National Association of Manufacturers has stated that enlightened management should have stable employment as one of its goals. The U.S. Chamber of Commerce has also included stable employment as a goal of industry. When this responsibility is neglected, all of us, including industry, suffer. I submit that a guaranteed annual wage would thus seem to be a fair and just method of attacking the evils of unemployment.

It is also a workable plan. Economically, it is very reasonable. The cost of a guaranteed annual wage plan would be similar to a moderate wage increase. The

Procter and Gamble Company plan, after 20 years, has never cost more than 3% of the payroll. The Ford plan calls for a company contribution of five cents per hour per man. This is not excessive in relation to the wage increases that have been granted recently. In fact, a guaranteed annual wage plan would seem feasible for any U.S. industry.

And the specific plan could be flexible enough to be adapted to the needs and problems of each industry. The Ford plan, again, provides an example. During the first week of a layoff, the worker receives no pay. During the next four weeks, he receives 65% of his base pay. Thereafter, he receives 60% of his base pay for a maximum of twenty-one weeks. Money comes out of the reserve fund created by the five cents per hour per man put in by the company. Payments last only as long as there is money in the reserve fund. Hopefully, the reserve will be big enough to cover all emergencies.

The Hormel Meat Packing Company of Austin, Minnesota, is another example. It has one of the oldest guaranteed annual wage plans in existence, very similar to Ford's. The main difference is that it includes the full 52 weeks, instead of 26. The American and Continental Can Co. granted its employees a full year plan in 1956, adapting the specific provisions to its own situation. The same is true of the Nunn-Bush Shoe Co. of Wisconsin, and many smaller companies. All in all, the principles involved in a guaranteed annual wage are neither excessively expensive nor too rigid to fit into all industries but form a reasonable and flexible plan that can work.

I ask each of you to lend your support to the guaranteed annual wage principle whenever and wherever you can. Remember, it will help solve the economic problem we now have. It will combat the evils of unemployment. It is fair and just to all. It is a workable plan.

Perhaps even more important, it will make it possible to meet future economic problems. *Life* magazine, Jan. 17, 1955, stated that the United States may be able to produce and consume at boom-time levels and still have permanent reserves of unemployment because of tremendous technological advances. *Nation's Business,* in Dec., 1954, declared that automation is bound to reduce the need for unskilled and semiskilled workers. We can't allow this growing possibility of increased unemployment to weaken, or destroy, our economy. Support a guaranteed annual wage.

Grossly Disorganized Speech

As you know, wages have continued to rise—right up to the present time. So already a guaranteed annual wage has been introduced into our society. This meant that each employee could be sure of at least a minimum income during the year regardless of how many days he worked.

Other companies in the automobile industry followed Ford's lead in this. This was one of the first real gains to be made by the laboring man. In the year 1914, Henry Ford surprised his competitors, and his employees, by raising the minimum wages of his factory workers from $2.34 a day to $5.00 a day. In 1955, Henry Ford II agreed, in principle, to a guaranteed annual wage for Ford Company employees. Of course, the more he worked the more he would earn, but he could count on a minimum income even if he were laid off temporarily. Other major auto manufacturers did the same. General Motors almost immediately adopted the same policy as Ford.

The American and Continental Can Co. granted its employees a full-year plan in 1955, adapting the specific provisions to its own situation. The cost of a guaranteed annual wage plan would be similar to a moderate wage increase. Economically, it is very reasonable. Payments last only as long as there is money in the reserve fund. One great effect is on industry itself. It is also a workable plan.

The Hormel Meat Packing Company of Austin, Minnesota, is another example. All in all, the principles involved in a guaranteed annual wage are neither excessively expensive nor too rigid to fit into all industries, but form a reasonable and flexible plan that can work. The National Association of Manufacturers has stated that enlightened management should have stable employment as one of its goals. It isn't just the working man who suffers when he's unemployed. Industrial production and profits must necessarily go down. And the specific plan could be flexible enough to be adapted to the needs and problems of each industry. But it is the grocer, the landlord, and the professional man who must bear the brunt of unpaid bills.

We find, for instance, that the typical working man has no savings to fall back on. When money is short, the consumer can't buy. So it is to industry's advantage to attack the problems of unemployment, and to our advantage to support such a program. Even in 1957, unemployment was one of our most pressing national problems. During the next four weeks, he receives 65% of his base pay. All in all, if we average unemployment during the peacetime years between 1900 and 1950, we find that an average of 8.4% of our working force was unemployed. I submit that a guaranteed annual wage would thus seem to be a fair and just method of attacking the evils of unemployment.

The same is true of the Nunn-Bush Shoe Co. of Wisconsin, and many smaller companies. The Procter and Gamble Co. plan, over 20 years old, has never cost more than 3% of the payroll. Eventually *all* of us are affected. Let's take a look at unemployment in the recent years. It has one of the oldest guaranteed annual wage plans in existence, very similar to Ford's. It is my purpose to discuss with you some aspects of the guaranteed annual wage and to urge your support of it.

Laboring men are consumers; so are the unpaid grocers and landlords. During the first week of a layoff, the worker receives no pay. When this responsibility is neglected, all of us, including industry suffer. Industry has already recognized its responsibility in this matter of unemployment. The Ford plan, again, provides an example. Money comes out of the reserve fund created by the five cents per hour per man put in by the company. He is immediately faced with the problem of survival. This is not excessive in relation to the wage increases that have been granted recently.

In 1950, a relatively prosperous year, 4½ million people were unemployed. Obviously, unemployment is a real problem. The main difference is that it includes the full 52 weeks, instead of 26. A means must be found to combat it, and a guaranteed annual wage will do just that. The U.S. Chamber of Commerce has also included stable employment as a goal of industry. The Ford plan calls for a company contribution of five cents per hour per man. In fact, a guaranteed annual wage plan would seem feasible for any U.S. industry.

In 1931–1932, 18 million people were unemployed. It is important to add that the guaranteed annual wage program is a fair and just method of attacking unemployment. In 1939, 9 million people were still unemployed. No doubt he is the hardest hit. Thereafter, he receives 60% of his base pay for a maximum of twenty-one weeks. Hopefully, the reserve will be big enough to cover all emergencies. The need for such a measure as the guaranteed annual wage is based on the one real weakness of our economy—unemployment.

Life magazine, Jan. 17, 1955, stated that the United States may be able to produce and consume at boom-time level and still have permanent reserves of unemployment because of tremendous technological advances. I ask each of you to lend your support to the guaranteed annual wage principle whenever and wherever you can. We can't allow this growing possibility of increased unemployment to weaken, or destroy, our economy. Remember, it will help solve the economic problem we now have. It is a workable plan. It is fair and just to all. Perhaps even more important, it will make it possible to meet future economic problems.

Nation's Business, in Dec., 1954, declared that automation is bound to reduce the need for unskilled and semiskilled workers. It will combat the evils of unemployment. Support a guaranteed annual wage.

Retention Test

On the basis of the speech you have just heard, please answer the following questions. They are all of the multiple-choice type. Choose the answer you consider the *best,* and circle the number.

1.   The Ford Company guaranteed annual wage plan requires the company to contribute: (1) 5% of the payroll; (2) 5 cents per day for each worker; (3) 5 cents per hour for each worker; (4) 5 cents per hour for each unemployed worker.

2.   The effect of unemployment is most severely felt by: (1) the laboring man; (2) professional man; (3) industry; (4) all of the above.

3.   If an employee is laid off at the Ford plant, he can draw up to what percentage of his wages: (1) 50%; (2) 55%; (3) 60%; (4) 65%.

4.   During 1950, unemployment reached what level: (1) 8½ million; (2) 6½ million; (3) 4½ million; (4) 2½ million.

5.   Which magazine predicted greater unemployment in the future: (1) *Look;* (2) *Nation's Business;* (3) *U.S. News & World Report;* (4) *Newsweek.*

6.   During the peacetime years between 1900 and 1950, approximately what was the average percentage of the working force unemployed each year: (1) 18%; (2) 12%; (3) 8½%; (4) 4½%.

7.   A guaranteed annual wage can be used in all industries because it is: (1) flexible; (2) comprehensive; (3) easy to initiate; (4) supplements other income.

8.   In 1931–1932, how many people were unemployed: (1) 25 million; (2) 18 million; (3) 12 million; (4) 8 million.

9.   Under the Ford Company guaranteed annual wage plan, payments to employees will last a maximum of: (1) 21 weeks; (2) 26 weeks; (3) 34 weeks; (4) 52 weeks.

10.   The Ford Company guaranteed annual wage plan is financed through: (1) a reserve fund set up for that purpose; (2) joint labor-management contributions; (3) industrial emergency funds; (4) all of the above.

11.   According to the Ford guaranteed annual wage plan, during the first week of layoff, an employee will be paid: (1) 65% of his wage; (2) 60% of his wage; (3) 50% of his wage; (4) none of the above.

12.   The Procter and Gamble plan is (1) 5 years old; (2) 10 years old; (3) 15 years old; (4) 20 years old.

13.   Henry Ford approximately doubled the wages of his employees in the year: (1) 1931; (2) 1914; (3) 1918; (4) 1921.

14.   Henry Ford II, as president of the Ford Company, agreed to the principle of a guaranteed annual wage in: (1) 1914; (2) 1939; (3) 1947; (4) 1955.

15. Henry Ford raised the wages of his employees to $5.00 a day from (1) $2.20 a day; (2) $2.34 a day; (3) $2.68 a day; (4) $2.84 a day.

16. In terms of its cost to industry, a guaranteed annual wage plan would be: (1) a heavy burden on industry; (2) a moderate expense; (3) no expense to industry; (4) absorbed by increased profits.

17. According to the Ford guaranteed annual wage plan, during the fifth week of a layoff a worker is paid: (1) 65% of his wage; (2) 60% of his wage; (3) 50% of his wage; (4) none of the above.

18. One of the earliest guaranteed annual wage plans was put into effect at: (1) American and Continental Can Company; (2) Ford Company; (3) Hormel Meat Packing Company; (4) General Motors.

19. The Procter and Gamble guaranteed annual wage plan has never cost more than: (1) 1% of the payroll; (2) 3% of the payroll; (3) 5% of the payroll; (4) 7% of the payroll.

20. One of the first real gains made by the laboring man was: (1) the guaranteed annual wage plan accepted by the automobile industry; (2) a wage increase granted by the Ford Company; (3) a guaranteed annual wage by the Ford Company; (4) a guaranteed annual wage by the steel industry.

21. The speaker wanted you to: (1) support the principle of a guaranteed annual wage; (2) support a guaranteed annual wage plan; (3) support a guaranteed annual wage plan similar to the Ford Company plan; (4) all of the above.

22. The main purpose of the speech you heard was: (1) to show that industry has violated its obligation to labor; (2) to show that unemployment is the cause of our economic trouble; (3) to show that a guaranteed annual wage is the best solution to unemployment; (4) to show that a guaranteed annual wage plan can work in all industries.

23. It was stated that a guaranteed annual wage meets the following criteria, *except* one. Which one was not mentioned: (1) it reduces the effects of unemployment; (2) it reduces the probability of recessions; (3) it is a fair plan; (4) it is a workable plan.

24. A guaranteed annual wage will help our economy by: (1) meeting future umeployment problems; (2) increasing worker incentive; (3) reducing labor unrest; (4) encouraging technological advancement.

25. A guaranteed annual wage can be used in all industries because it is: (1) flexible; (2) comprehensive; (3) easy to initiate; (4) supplements other income.

26. A guaranteed annual wage is needed because: (1) of the inherent evils of unemployment; (2) it is a fair and just plan; (3) it is workable; (4) industry hasn't faced up to the problem.

27. According to the speaker, a guaranteed annual wage is important because of: (1) seasonable unemployment; (2) depressions; (3) unemployment caused by technical advances; (4) all of the above.

28. It was stated that a guaranteed annual wage should be supported because it was: (1) convenient; (2) workable; (3) the only solution; (4) none of the above.

Chapter 4
Message Preparation and Presentation

Message preparation and presentation concerns the ways in which a person selects, arranges, supports, amplifies, and displays the materials that constitute a message. Studies dealing with how messages are prepared and presented assume that it is possible consciously to design a message in order to enhance its effectiveness. These studies focus on how the retention of information and the persuasiveness of appeals are affected by the message structure, the arguments, and the style of language, among other things.

Experiment 4.1
Presenting Evidence

Proposition

Messages that employ emotional appeals are sometimes more effective than messages that employ rational arguments.

Research Questions

By using evidence, does a speaker convince his or her audience of the validity of a proposition?

Does giving the source of evidence produce changes in attitudes?

Research Methods*

Subjects

Forty randomly selected subjects, or two sections of a basic course with 40 students. Twenty of these subjects constitute each of two audiences.

*Adapted from an experiment reported in Robert S. Cathcart, "An Experimental Study of the Relative Effectiveness of Four Methods of Presenting Evidence," *Speech Monographs,* Vol. 22 (August 1955), pp. 227–233, and James C. McCroskey, "Experimental Studies of the Effects of Ethos and Evidence in Persuasive Communication," Ed.D. dissertation, Pennsylvania State University, 1966. By permission.

Materials

Two copies of an Opinion Ballot for each subject, one for the pretest and one for the posttest.

Two tape-recorded speeches on the topic of education. The speeches should be recorded from the manuscript by the same person. One speech (Speech A) contains carefully documented evidence, and the other (Speech B) contains no evidence and no reference to sources.

Tape recorder for playing the speeches.

Small table on which to place the tape recorder.

Procedures

1. Selection and Preparation of Subjects
   a. Arrange with instructors to use courses or sections with the desired number of subjects.
   b. Four weeks prior to the experiment, administer the Opinion Ballot (pretest) to all participating subjects.
   c. Arrange for a specific time to play the speeches to the subjects; Speech A (documented evidence) should be played for one audience, and Speech B (no evidence) should be played to the other audience at a different time.
2. Conduct of the Experiment
   a. In the same room in which audience A is to assemble, set up a small table, on which you place the tape recorder with Speech A.
   b. As soon as the audience is assembled, explain that they will be listening to a recorded speech, after which they will be asked to complete the Opinion Ballot (posttest).
   c. Play the speech.
   d. Turn off the tape recorder, and ask the subjects to complete the opinion ballot.
   e. Collect the ballots and questionnaires.
   f. Follow the same procedure for audience B, using the no-evidence speech.
3. Tabulation of the Data
   a. Assign numbers from 1 to 7 to the responses on the Opinion Ballot, with Strongly Agree number 1 and Strongly Disagree number 7.
   b. Total these numbers for each subject on the 22 statements on the ballot for both the pretest and the posttest.
   c. Record the pre- and posttest scores, and determine the difference. Use the data tabulation chart on page 87.

Subject	Documented Evidence			No Evidence		
	Prescore	Postscore	Difference	Prescore	Postscore	Difference
1						
2						
3						
4						
5						
6						
7						
8						
9						
10						
11						
12						
13						
14						
15						
16						
17						
18						
19						
20						

Differences between Pre- and Postscores

Name _____   Section _____

Date _____   Instructor _____

Results

1. What differences occurred between the two speeches in terms of opinion shift?

2. Which speech seemed to produce the largest amount of opinion shift, for which group, and what factors seem to account for the shift?

Explanation

1. Write a concise summary of this experiment and the results obtained.

2. Based on the results of this study, what advice would you give to a speaker about presenting ideas and information in a speech? Is evidence important? Is it important to document sources?

Opinion Ballot

Instructions: This is a study of attitudes toward education. It is *not* a test. You will find twenty-two statements below that express different attitudes toward education. Please indicate your opinion of each of the statements by checking the number that best describes your view on each of the scales.

1. Quality in education can best be guaranteed by local school boards.

Strongly Agree ___ : ___ : ___ : ___ : ___ : ___ : ___ Strongly Disagree
      1   2   3   4   5   6   7

2. Public schools should be financed primarily by federal taxes.

Strongly Agree ___ : ___ : ___ : ___ : ___ : ___ : ___ Strongly Disagree
      1   2   3   4   5   6   7

3. Equality of opportunity in education for all citizens can be best guaranteed by federal control of education.

Strongly Agree ___ : ___ : ___ : ___ : ___ : ___ : ___ Strongly Disagree
      1   2   3   4   5   6   7

4. The curriculum of public schools should be determined by local school boards.

Strongly Agree ___ : ___ : ___ : ___ : ___ : ___ : ___ Strongly Disagree
      1   2   3   4   5   6   7

5. The federal government should have no control over the curriculum of public schools.

Strongly Agree ___ : ___ : ___ : ___ : ___ : ___ : ___ Strongly Disagree
      1   2   3   4   5   6   7

6. Public schools can be administered better by the federal government than by local school boards.

Strongly Agree ___ : ___ : ___ : ___ : ___ : ___ : ___ Strongly Disagree
      1   2   3   4   5   6   7

7. Quality in education can best be guaranteed by the federal government.

Strongly Agree ___ : ___ : ___ : ___ : ___ : ___ : ___ Strongly Disagree
      1   2   3   4   5   6   7

8. The curriculum of public schools should be determined by the federal government.

Strongly Agree ___ : ___ : ___ : ___ : ___ : ___ : ___ Strongly Disagree
      1   2   3   4   5   6   7

9. Equality of opportunity in education for all citizens can be best guaranteed by local control of education.

Strongly Agree ___ : ___ : ___ : ___ : ___ : ___ : ___ Strongly Disagree
            1   2   3   4   5   6   7

10. Public schools should be financed primarily by local taxes.

Strongly Agree ___ : ___ : ___ : ___ : ___ : ___ : ___ Strongly Disagree
            1   2   3   4   5   6   7

11. The federal government should assume complete financial responsibility for education.

Strongly Agree ___ : ___ : ___ : ___ : ___ : ___ : ___ Strongly Disagree
            1   2   3   4   5   6   7

12. Public schools can be administered better by local school boards than by the federal government.

Strongly Agree ___ : ___ : ___ : ___ : ___ : ___ : ___ Strongly Disagree
            1   2   3   4   5   6   7

13. The amount of teachers' salaries should be determined by the federal government.

Strongly Agree ___ : ___ : ___ : ___ : ___ : ___ : ___ Strongly Disagree
            1   2   3   4   5   6   7

14. Teacher employment standards should be controlled by local school boards.

Strongly Agree ___ : ___ : ___ : ___ : ___ : ___ : ___ Strongly Disagree
            1   2   3   4   5   6   7

15. Public schools should not be primarily financed by local taxes.

Strongly Agree ___ : ___ : ___ : ___ : ___ : ___ : ___ Strongly Disagree
            1   2   3   4   5   6   7

16. The amount of teachers' salaries should be determined by local school boards.

Strongly Agree ___ : ___ : ___ : ___ : ___ : ___ : ___ Strongly Disagree
            1   2   3   4   5   6   7

17. The federal government should have no control over teacher employment standards.

Strongly Agree ___ : ___ : ___ : ___ : ___ : ___ : ___ Strongly Disagree
            1   2   3   4   5   6   7

18. The federal government should substantially increase its financial support of public education.

Strongly Agree ___ : ___ : ___ : ___ : ___ : ___ : ___ Strongly Disagree
            1   2   3   4   5   6   7

19. The federal government should not determine the amount of teachers' salaries.

Strongly Agree ___ : ___ : ___ : ___ : ___ : ___ : ___ Strongly Disagree
           1   2   3   4   5   6   7

20. Teacher employment standards should be controlled by the federal government.

Strongly Agree ___ : ___ : ___ : ___ : ___ : ___ : ___ Strongly Disagree
           1   2   3   4   5   6   7

21. Public schools should not be primarily financed by federal taxes.

Strongly Agree ___ : ___ : ___ : ___ : ___ : ___ : ___ Strongly Disagree
           1   2   3   4   5   6   7

22. Local school boards should not determine the amount of teachers' salaries.

Strongly Agree ___ : ___ : ___ : ___ : ___ : ___ : ___ Strongly Disagree
           1   2   3   4   5   6   7

Education Speech (A): With Evidence

Almost two hundred years ago Thomas Jefferson told the American people that if we expected to remain both ignorant and free we were expecting what never was and never will be. If it was true that man could not remain ignorant and free in the 18th century, it is even truer today. Thus it is not surprising that almost every American will tell you that he is "all for the best educational system possible." With this historical support and apparently favorable modern attitude, we could be led to the assumption that the United States has the best possible public educational system already in operation. Before we accept this assumption as fact, we should determine just what are the criteria for the best possible educational system for the 20th century and how well our present system measures up to this ideal. It will be my purpose to do just that.

While there may be some disagreement on the order of importance, most people concerned with our educational system would suggest four criteria for a first-class program. First, the quality of the instruction must be high. Second, there must be adequate finances available to provide for all legitimate educational needs. Third, the school system must provide equal opportunity for all children in the nation. Finally, qualified people must control the operation of the system. Let's look at these criteria of the ideal school system to see what they really mean and how our present school system in the United States meets or fails to meet them.

Probably the most difficult thing to define in relation to education is quality. But I think we can assume that whatever quality is, it will be present if students take the right courses from well-trained teachers. Of course, who is to say what are the "right" courses? In any given school we will find students with differing abilities and interests. Thus, different courses are needed by different students in every school. The right courses for some students are rigorous college preparatory subjects while for others vocational training courses are what are most appropriate. The important thing in assessing the quality of an educational system is whether or not individual students, whatever school they must attend, are able to study the courses that are right for them. Unfortunately, in many of our nation's schools, students are not able to take the right courses—simply because they aren't even offered. According to figures released by the Department of Health, Education, and Welfare of the federal government, over one-third of the nation's high schools do not offer such essential college preparatory subjects as chemistry or physics, and about the same number don't offer even one foreign language. Only a small fraction of our public schools offer a broad program of vocational education. From this we must conclude that many of our students are not obtaining the quality education we desire.

But, for a moment, let us assume that every student in the United States has the opportunity to take the right courses. We still will be forced to conclude that the quality of American education is not acceptable because of that second characteristic of a quality educational system that I mentioned a few moments ago—well-trained teachers. I'm sure I don't have to tell anyone about the tremendous shortage of adequately trained teachers. Almost every state is presently forced to accept substandard teachers. In their report entitled *The Financial Status of Public Schools* the Committee on Educational Finance of the National Education Association reports that last year the nation was short 118,000 qualified teachers just to meet *minimum* standards. We can only guess what that figure would be if we tried to eliminate all of the incompetent teachers in the classrooms today and replace them with thoroughly trained and qualified individuals. I would suggest 500,000 as a very conservative starting figure. But, whatever the figure is, since many needed courses are not even offered students in many of our schools and we face a serious shortage of competent teachers, we must conclude that our present educational system falls far short of our ideal of a quality educational system.

Now let us turn our attention to the criterion of finance. We can't set down an exact figure and say this or that amount of money is adequate for a first-class educational system. No one is in a position to be that exact. However, we can say that if our schools have enough money to provide educationally acceptable physical plants, to pay professional salaries to our teachers, and to cover costs of operating expenses and equipment, that could be called adequate finance. Unfortunately, many of our school districts do not have that kind of money.

Let us look first at physical plants. According to figures released by the United States Office of Education in January of this year, 25.4% of the nation's classrooms are, in their words, "obsolete and unacceptable" for public schools because of such things as extreme fire hazards. Translating that percentage into numbers of classrooms, we find that over 375,000 classrooms are presently unacceptable. In terms of students, this means that over nine million American children are presently attending substandard schools, some of which the U. S. Office of Education calls "fire hazards." But one may ask, "Isn't this problem being overcome?" Unfortunately, it isn't in many areas. I needn't point out that most schools are built by finances derived by selling municipal bonds. These bond issues must be voted on by the people in the communities involved. If the bonds are voted down, the new school facilities are not built. The U. S. Office of Education reports that 28% of the bond issues for such facilities were defeated between 1957 and 1963. The figure rose to 31% last year. It is apparent from these figures that not only are there numerous school buildings in completely unacceptable condition, but even in those communities where an attempt is made to remedy the problem, over a fourth of the attempts are unsuccessful.

And how about adequate financing to provide for professional salaries for our teachers? Well, let's look at the facts and then decide for ourselves. The most recent national study of teachers' salaries was released January 3, 1965, by the National Education Association. This material was included in the *NEA Research Report 1964 R17*. We find that the average elementary school teacher in the United States earns just over $6,000. The average in California is over $7,500. However, in Mississippi and South Dakota it is only $4,000. Figures for secondary school teachers are similar. The national average is $6,500, with California leading the country with an average of $8,400 and Mississippi bringing up the rear with an average of under $4,300. Probably many of us have enough information already to draw a conclusion about the adequacy of financing in some of our states like Mississippi and South Dakota. But let's get away from state and national "averages" and look at teachers' salaries from another perspective. Most of us know that the generally accepted income level under which people are considered to be living in abject poverty is $3,000. Certainly a professional educator should be expected to earn far more than that. However, according to figures from that same *NEA Research Report, 1964 R17,* 23% of the teachers in South Dakota earn less than $3,500. Thirty-one percent of the teachers in Arkansas earn less than that figure. Then, of course, there is Mississippi. Only 14% of Mississippi's teachers earn less than $3,500. This wouldn't seem too bad if it weren't for the fact that 80% of Mississippi's teachers earn less than $4,500. This compares with New York, Pennsylvania, Arizona, California, Nevada, and Alaska, which have *no* teachers making less than $4,500.

Now, don't misunderstand me. Some teachers make a fairly good income, but their salaries just don't compare with other occupations requiring a college degree. The average college graduate, according to a survey conducted by Elmer Roper and Associates, can expect to earn an annual salary of about $7,500 after three years on the job. According to figures reported in the *NEA Research Report* I mentioned before, in three states, New York, California, and Alaska, over 20% of the teachers earn more than that figure. But on the other side of the ledger, in thirteen states less than 1% of the teachers receive such a salary; seven of these states have *no* teacher making that amount.

Thus, while some schools in some areas have excellent financing, other schools in other areas are fire hazards staffed by teachers receiving salaries which force them to live in what our government calls "abject poverty." I don't know what conclusion you will draw from these facts, but I can only conclude that the present financing of our public schools is very inadequate.

But, we cannot complete our evaluation of the present school system in the United States without considering the criterion of equality of opportunity for all of our children. There are several things that we must consider in determining whether equality of opportunity is present, some of which I have already mentioned. For a national educational system that offers equal opportunity to all of its children, course offerings must be somewhat similar across the country. We have already seen that this isn't the case in American education. Also for equality of opportunity to exist, the teachers should be reasonably comparable from one area to another. But it would be stretching the imagination pretty far to suggest that Mississippi can get as high a quality of teachers for $3,000 as California can for $8,000. Finally, we must mention that many of our children are still prohibited from achieving equality of opportunity in education because of race. Governor Johnson of Mississippi during the last election bragged that no school in the state of Mississippi was integrated. There has been some improvement since then. Now only a little over 99% are segregated.

Truly, equality of opportunity in American education is nothing but a dream, a dream that will *never* come true as long as the Johnsons, the Wallaces, and their kind control education.

This brings us to the last criterion for an ideal public educational system that I posited early in this talk, that qualified people must be in control of the system. Well, what is a qualified person? I would suggest that three characteristics are essential. Such a person should, among other things, be well educated, he should understand the process of curriculum building, and he should have a thorough understanding of modern teaching procedures. Let's look at who is actually in control of our schools. As we all know, the local school board is in charge of our schools, so we need to determine whether these people are capable of properly running an educational system.

First, we can consider what the requirements are for a person to become a school board member. According to *Bulletin 1957–13* of the U. S. Office of Education, entitled "Provisions Governing Membership on Local Boards of Education," the picture is not encouraging. Not one single state requires that a school board member know anything at all about education! In twenty-six states the only requirement is that the person be a qualified voter. Ten others have additional residence requirements. Eleven require an eighth grade education. Four require that the board member be a taxpayer or parent. And, one state, Rhode Island, has no requirements at all.

From this we might suspect that our boards are made up of people totally unqualified to run an educational system. Such a suspicion is borne out in fact. From that same U. S. Office of Education report that I mentioned a moment ago we find that the U.S.O.E. national survey of school boards determined that 23.8% of the nation's school boards include people who are not even high school graduates. In the South the figure is 41%. People who haven't even finished high school are telling our teachers not only what to teach but how to teach it. Some people are concerned about the future of high school dropouts. It seems that we have little cause for concern. They will just grow up to be tomorrow's school board members!

Of course, some school board members have finished high school, so let's look at the occupations of school board members in general. Again citing official U. S. Office of Education figures, we find that 35% of the school board members are business owners, officials, and managers. Twenty-seven percent are in the professional and technical services—doctors, lawyers, and engineers. Twelve percent are farmers, 9% are laborers and craftsmen, 7% are housewives, and 7% are clerks. Did you notice one group missing from that list? I did. Educators! There were so few qualified educators that were members of local school boards that the U. S. Office of Education did not even report them as a separate category.

I think it says something significant about our nation's attitude toward education that we let just anyone serve on our school boards. It is even state law in most states that a man must be a licensed veterinarian to take care of our sick dogs. But our children's schools? Anyone is capable of taking care of them. Well, I, for one, refuse to buy that attitude. I think it is time that we make some drastic revisions in our American educational system. The place to begin is right at the heart of the present system, with the people who are controlling the schools, the ones who are responsible for the present deplorable state of American education. These problems cannot be overcome by merely increasing federal aid to education as some people suggest. Turning money over to states like Mississippi and Alabama won't solve anything. Neither will it be of any help to turn over federal money to local school districts run by school boards composed of school dropouts. The only answer is to do for our children's schools what we have done for our dogs—turn them over to trained, qualified, experts and provide the money needed to properly educate American youth to take its place in the space age.

More specifically, I suggest that it is time for the federal government to assume ultimate control of the educational system of the United States. This is not to suggest that we turn the schools over to the federal politicians; rather it is to take them away from the *local* politicians and turn them over to the educators. The specific proposal that I recommend is very similar to the one first suggested by Carl J. Megel, president of the American Federation of Teachers, in testimony before the Committee on Education and Labor of the U. S. House of Representatives when that committee was considering the late President Kennedy's program for public education in 1962. This program has three major points:

First, it should be established by law that 10% of all future federal budgets be devoted to American public school education. Along with this law, provision should be made for establishing an absolute priority for education before all other expenditures of the government. California now has such a provision and leads the nation in almost every area of education.

Second, the federal government should assume all present debts of public schools. This would equalize the program so that communities that have gone into debt to build present schools would not be penalized for that action.

Finally, a national council on education should be formed composed of members of the National Education Association and the education associations of the fifty states. This council would serve as advisors to the U. S. Office of Education, which would be exclusively empowered to dispense all funds for education in the United States. This would not only guarantee standardization of the educational system across the U. S. but would also guarantee that the special needs of the state and locality would be served by that state's education association representatives. In short, the ultimate *control* of education would be in the hands of the federal government, but the *operation* of the schools would be left to professional educators hired on the state and local level.

What would be the effect of this program? Well, let's turn to the criteria for an ideal school system that I mentioned a while ago to see how well this program would stand up. First, we said that the quality of education must be high. Since under the program I have recommended our schools would all be part of one standardized system, each student would have the opportunity to take the courses most suited to his needs, wherever he lives. Since there would be no shortage of funds, top-flight people would be drawn into the teaching profession by truly adequate professional salaries. As we noted before, if a student takes the right courses from qualified teachers we have what can only be described as quality education. Second, we said that a school system should have adequate finances available to provide for all legitimate educational needs. If the budget and priority for education that I have recommended is adopted, no educational decisions will be dependent on financial considerations. The only important thing will be "Is it needed?" If salaries are too low, they will be increased. If a classroom building is a fire hazard, it will be replaced. If a teacher needs a slide projector or a tape recorder for her class, it will be provided.

It is important to note one more thing in this regard. Today, in most communities when the school budget is increased, the property owners are forced to pay most of the bill through property taxes. These taxes are excessively high already in most areas and can't be expected to be increased much more. People on stable incomes just can't pay these exorbitant taxes. The people hurt most are the retired people and widows who own their homes but have little or no income. Under the program I have suggested this oppressive form of taxation would not be needed and so could be abolished. All funds for education would come from federal taxes which are based on a person's ability to pay, not on where he lives or what he owns.

Thus, under this system, the financial needs of education would be met, and, at the same time, an oppressive tax would be removed and replaced by the most democratic type of tax system. Certainly under such a program, we can say that the criterion of "adequate" financing will be met.

Our third criterion was that the school system must provide equal opportunity for all children in the nation. Under the program I have suggested the facilities would be equal, the teachers would be relatively equal, and the course offerings would be equal. But most significantly, *only* under a program such as I offer can we ever hope to have racial equality in education in many parts of the nation. It should be abundantly clear to anyone who is concerned enough to look at the situation in the South that under state and local control of education, Negro children will never be truly equal.

Finally, we said that our school system should be controlled by qualified individuals. Such people should be well educated, have a thorough knowledge of curriculum building, and an understanding of modern teaching procedures. The only people who have these characteristics are professional educators, precisely those people who would be administering our public school system under my program.

But what are the possible objections to this new program for American education that I have suggested? The most obvious objection is that it costs a lot of money. It certainly does. To make up for the neglect of our schools over the past fifty years is bound to be expensive. But any country that can afford $40 billion to put a man on the moon can certainly afford to educate its children.

Of course, the other objection is that this program is socialistic. It certainly is. *Public* schools by definition are socialistic institutions. The only question is whether we want this socialistic institution controlled at the local level by high school dropouts, the state level by men like Governors Wallace of Alabama and Johnson of Mississippi, or at the national level by professional educators. To me that choice is simple. I think it is to most thinking Americans, no matter what their political persuasion.

In the final determination we have to decide whether we, the richest nation on the face of the earth, wish to have an educational system capable of meeting the needs of our youth, or whether we are going to continue to sacrifice our children's future on the Altar of Irresponsibility.

Education Speech (B): Without Evidence

Almost two hundred years ago Thomas Jefferson told the American people that if we expected to remain both ignorant and free we were expecting what never was and never will be. If it was true that man could not remain ignorant and free in the 18th century, it is truer today. Thus it is not surprising that almost every American will tell you that he is "all for the best educational system possible." With this historical support and apparently favorable modern attitude, we could be led to the assumption that the United States has the best possible public educational system already in operation. Before we accept this assumption as fact, we should determine just what are the criteria for the best possible educational system for the 20th century and how well our present system measures up to this ideal. It will be my purpose this evening to do just that.

While there may be some disagreement on the order of importance, most people concerned with our educational system would suggest four criteria for a first-class program. First, the quality of the instruction must be high. Second, there must be adequate finances available to provide for all legitimate educational needs. Third, the school system must provide equal opportunity for all children in the nation. Finally, qualified people must control the operation of the system. Let's look at these criteria of the ideal school system to see what they really mean and how our present school system in the United States meets or fails to meet them.

Probably the most difficult thing to define in relation to education is quality. But I think we can assume that whatever quality is, it will be present if students take the right courses from well-trained teachers. Of course, who is to say what are the "right" courses? In any given school we will find students with differing abilities and interests. Thus, different courses are needed by different students in every school. The right courses for some students are rigorous college preparatory subjects while for others vocational training courses are what are most appropriate. The important thing in assessing the quality of an educational system is whether or not individual students, whatever school they must attend, are able to study the courses that are right from them. Unfortunately, in many of our nation's schools students are not able to take the right courses—simply because they aren't even offered. Many of our schools do not offer such essential college preparatory subjects as chemistry or physics, and others don't offer even one foreign language. Only a small fraction of our public schools offer a broad program of vocational education. From this we must conclude that many of our students are not obtaining the quality education we desire.

But, for a moment, let us assume that every student in the United States has the opportunity to take the right courses. We still will be forced to conclude that the quality of American education is not acceptable because of that second characteristic of a quality educational system that I mentioned a few moments ago —well-trained teachers. I'm sure I don't have to tell anyone about the tremendous shortage of adequately trained teachers. Almost every state is presently forced to accept substandard teachers. Across the nation we are short more than 100,000 teachers just to meet *minimum* standards. We can only guess what the figure would be if we tried to eliminate all of the incompetent teachers in the classrooms today and replace them with thoroughly trained and qualified individuals. I would suggest 500,000 as a very conservative starting figure. But, whatever the figure is, since many needed courses are not even offered students in many of our schools, and we face a serious shortage of competent teachers, we must conclude that our present educational system falls far short of our ideal of a quality educational system.

Now let us turn our attention to the criterion of finance. We can't set down an exact figure and say this or that amount of money is adequate for a first-class educational system. No one is in a position to be that exact. However, we can say that if our schools have enough money to provide educationally acceptable physical plants, to pay professional salaries to our teachers, and to cover costs of operating expenses and equipment, that could be called adequate finance. Unfortunately, many of our school districts do not have that kind of money.

Let us look first at physical plants. A very large percentage of the classrooms presently in use are obsolete and unacceptable for public schools because of such things as extreme fire hazards. Over 300,000 of our present classrooms are unacceptable. This means that upwards of 9 million American children are forced to attend substandard schools, some of which are so bad that they can only be classed as fire hazards. But one may ask, "Isn't this problem being overcome?" Unfortunately it isn't in many areas. I needn't point out that most schools are built by finances derived by selling municipal bonds. These bond issues must be voted on by the people in the communities involved. If the bonds are voted down, the new school facilities are not built. Almost one-fourth of these bond issues have been voted down in elections over the past few years, and the number is increasing. It is apparent from these facts that not only are there numerous school buildings in completely unacceptable condition, but even in those communities where an attempt is made to remedy the problem, over a fourth of the attempts are unsuccessful.

And how about adequate financing to provide for professional salaries for our teachers? Probably many of us have enough information already to draw a conclusion about the adequacy of financing in some of our states. We know that the average teacher's salary in some states is only half of that of teachers in other states. But let's get away from state and national "averages" and look at teachers' salaries from another perspective. Most of us know that the generally accepted income level under which people are considered to be living in abject poverty is $3,000. Certainly a professional educator should be expected to earn far more than that. However, in some states many teachers receive salaries below that level.

Now, don't misunderstand me. In some states teachers make a fairly good income. But very few teachers receive salaries comparable to other college graduates. It all depends on what state in which the teacher happens to live whether he receives an adequate salary or is forced to live on a near-poverty level.

Thus, while some schools in some areas have excellent financing, other schools in other areas are fire hazards staffed by teachers receiving salaries which force them to live in what our government calls "abject poverty." I don't know what conclusion you will draw from these facts, but I can only conclude that the present financing of our public schools is very inadequate.

But we cannot complete our evaluation of the present school system in the United States without considering the criterion of equality of opportunity for all of our children. There are several things that we must consider in determining whether equality of opportunity is present, some of which I have already mentioned. For a national educational system that offers equal opportunity to all of its children, course offerings must be somewhat similar across the country. We have already seen that this isn't the case in American education. Also for equality of opportunity to exist, the teachers should be reasonably comparable from one area to another. But it would be stretching the imagination pretty far to suggest that Mississippi can get as high a quality of teachers for $3,000 as California can for $8,000. Finally, we must mention that many of our children are still prohibited from achieving equality of opportunity in education because of race. Governor Johnson of Mississippi during the last election bragged that no school in the state of Mississippi was integrated. There has been some improvement since then. Now only a little over 99% are segregated.

Truly, equality of opportunity in American education is nothing but a dream, a dream that will *never* come true as long as the Johnsons, the Wallaces, and their kind control education.

This brings us to the last criterion for an ideal public educational system that I posited early in this talk, that qualified people must be in control of the system. Well, what is a qualified person? I would suggest that three characteristics are essential. Such a person should, among other things, be well educated, he should understand the process of curriculum building, and he should have a thorough understanding of modern teaching procedures. Let's look at who is actually in control of our schools. As we all know, the local school board is in charge of our schools, so we need to determine whether these people are capable of properly running an educational system.

First, we can consider what the requirements are for a person to become a school board member. The picture is not encouraging. No state requires that a school board member know anything about education. In most states the only requirement is that the person be a qualified voter. Some have additional residence requirements. Others require an eighth grade education. A few require that the board member be a taxpayer or parent. In some areas there are no requirements at all.

From this we might suspect that our boards are made up of people totally unqualified to run an educational system. Such a suspicion is borne out in fact. Many of the school boards in the United States include members who are not even high school graduates. People who haven't even finished high school are telling our teachers not only what to teach but how to teach it. Some people are concerned about the future of high school dropouts. It seems that we have little cause for concern. They will just grow up to be tomorrow's school board members!

Of course, some school board members have finished high school, so let's look at the occupations of school board members in general. Many of them are business owners, officials, and managers. Some are in the professional and technical services—doctors, lawyers, and engineers. Some are farmers. A few are laborers, craftsmen, housewives, and clerks. Did you notice one group missing from that list? I did. Educators! There are so few qualified educators that are members of local school boards that they don't even constitute a reportable category.

I think it says something significant about our nation's attitude toward education that we let just anyone serve on our school boards. It is even state law in most states that a man must be a licensed veterinarian to take care of our sick dogs. But our children's schools? Anyone is capable of taking care of them. Well, I, for one, refuse to buy that attitude. I think it is time that we make some drastic revisions in our American educational system. The place to begin is right at the heart of the present system, with the people who are controlling the schools, the ones who are responsible for the present deplorable state of American education. These problems cannot be overcome by merely increasing federal aid to education, as some people suggest. Turning money over to states like Mississippi and Alabama won't solve anything. Neither will it be of any help to turn over federal money to local school districts run by school boards composed of school dropouts. The only answer is to do for our children's schools what we have done for our dogs —turn them over to trained, qualified experts and provide the money needed to properly educate American youth to take its place in the space age.

More specifically, I suggest that it is time for the federal government to assume ultimate control of the educational system of the United States. This is not to suggest that we turn the schools over to the federal politicians; rather it is to take them away from the *local* politicians and turn them over to the educators. The specific proposal that I recommend has three major points.

First, it should be established by law that 10% of all future federal budgets be devoted to American public school education. Along with this law, provision should be made for establishing an absolute priority for education before all other expenditures of the government. California now has such a provision and leads the nation in almost every area of education.

Second, the federal government should assume all present debts of public schools. This would equalize the program so that communities that have gone into debt to build present schools would not be penalized for that action.

Finally, a national council on education should be formed composed of members of the National Education Association and the education associations of the fifty states. This council would serve as advisors to the U.S. Office of Education, which would be exclusively empowered to dispense all funds for education in the United States. This would not only guarantee standardization of the educational system across the U.S. but would also guarantee that the special needs of the state and locality would be served by that state's education association representatives. In short, the ultimate *control* of education would be in the hands of the federal government, but the *operation* of the schools would be left to professional educators hired on the state and local level.

What would be the effect of this program? Well, let's return to the criteria for an ideal school system that I mentioned a while ago to see how well this program would stand up. First, we said that the quality of education must be high. Since under the program I have recommended our schools would all be part of one standardized system, each student would have the opportunity to take the courses most suited to his needs, wherever he lives. Since there would be no shortage of funds, top-flight people would be drawn into the teaching profession by truly adequate professional salaries. As we noted before, if a student takes the right courses from qualified teachers, we have what can only be described as quality education. Second, we said that a school system should have adequate finances available to provide for all legitimate educational needs. If the budget and priority for education that I have recommended is adopted, no educational decisions will be dependent on financial considerations. The only important thing will be "Is it needed?" If salaries are too low, they will be increased. If a classroom building is a fire hazard, it will be replaced. If a teacher needs a slide projector or a tape recorder for her class, it will be provided.

It is important to note one more thing in this regard. Today, in most communities when the school budget is increased, the property owners are forced to pay most of the bill through property taxes. These taxes are excessively high already in most areas and can't be expected to be increased much more. People on stable incomes just can't pay these exorbitant taxes. The people hurt most are the retired people and widows who own their homes but have little or no income. Under the program I have suggested this oppressive form of taxation would not be needed and so could be abolished. All funds for education would come from federal taxes which are based on a person's ability to pay, not on where he lives or what he owns.

Thus, under this system, the financial needs of education would be met, and, at the same time, an oppressive tax would be removed and replaced by the most democratic type of tax system. Certainly under such a program, we can say that the criterion of "adequate" financing will be met.

Our third criterion was that the school system must provide equal opportunity for all children in the nation. Under the program I have suggested the facilities would be equal, the teachers would be relatively equal, and the course offerings would be equal. But most significantly, *only* under a program such as I offer can we ever hope to have racial equality in education in many parts of the nation. It should be abundantly clear to anyone who is concerned enough to look at the situation in the South that under state and local control of education, Negro children will never be truly equal.

Finally, we said that our school system should be controlled by qualified individuals. Such people should be well educated, have a thorough knowledge of curriculum building, and an understanding of modern teaching procedures. The only people who have these characteristics are professional educators, precisely those people who would be administering our public school system under my program.

But what are the possible objections to this new program for American education that I have suggested? The most obvious objection is that it costs a lot of money. It certainly does. To make up for the neglect of our schools over the past fifty years is bound to be expensive. But any country that can afford $40 billion to put a man on the moon can certainly afford to educate its children.

Of course, the other objection is that this program is socialistic. It certainly is. *Public* schools by definition are socialistic institutions. The only question is whether we want this socialistic institution controlled at the local level by high school dropouts, the state level by men like Governors Wallace of Alabama and Johnson of

Mississippi, or at the national level by professional educators. To me that choice is simple. I think it is to most thinking Americans, no matter what their political persuasion.

In the final determination, we have to decide whether we, the richest nation on the face of the earth, wish to have an educational system capable of meeting the needs of our youth, or whether we are going to continue to sacrifice our children's future on the Altar of Irresponsibility.

Experiment 4.2
Fear-Arousing Appeals

Proposition

Messages that employ minimal fear-arousing appeals tend to be more effective than those that arouse intense anxiety.

Research Questions

Does a speech containing reassuring recommendations to reduce anxiety tend to be remembered better?

Does such a speech produce greater shifts of opinion than one that does not contain a reassuring recommendation?

Research Methods*

Subjects

Forty randomly selected subjects or two sections of a basic course with 40 students. Twenty of the subjects constitute each of two groups.

Materials

Two tape-recorded speeches about 15 minutes long on the same topic. The speeches should be recorded from the manuscript by the same person. One speech is designed to produce fear and concludes without reassuring recommendations. The other speech is the same as the first one but concludes with reassuring recommendations.

Survey of Attitudes 1 (40 copies).

Survey of Attitudes 2 (40 copies).

Speaker Evaluation Form (40 copies).

Tape recorder for playing the speeches.

Small table on which to place the tape recorder.

Procedures

1. Selection and Preparation of Subjects
    a. Arrange with instructors to use courses or sections with the desired number of subjects.
    b. One week prior to the experiment, administer the Survey of Attitudes 1 to all participating subjects.
    c. Arrange for a specific time to play the speeches to the subjects. The speech text with the nonreassuring conclusion should be played for one group of

*Adapted from an experiment reported in Frances Cope and Don Richardson, "The Effects of Reassuring Recommendations in a Fear-Arousing Speech," *Speech Monographs*, Vol. 39 (June 1972), pp. 148–150. By permission.

subjects; at a different time, the speech text with the reassuring conclusion should be played for the second group of subjects.

2. Conduct of the Experiment
   a. Set up a small table on which a tape recorder is placed with the speech text and the nonreassuring conclusion.
   b. As soon as the subjects are assembled, explain that they are going to listen to a recorded speech, after which they will be asked to complete the Survey of Attitudes 2 and a Speaker Evaluation Form.
   c. Play the speech.
   d. Turn off the tape recorder, and ask the subjects to complete the Survey of Attitudes 2 and the Speaker Evaluation Form.
   e. Collect the survey and form.
   f. Follow the same procedure for the subjects hearing the speech with the reassuring conclusion.

3. Tabulation of the Data
   a. Sum the scores of subjects on item no. 4 for the Survey of Attitudes 1 and on item no. 4 for the Survey of Attitudes 2. Calculate the difference.

	Attitude Scale Scores		
	Item 4 (1)	Item 4 (2)	Difference
Nonreassuring			
Reassuring			

   b. Sum the scores for all subjects on item no. 13 and item no. 14 for the Survey of Attitudes 2, and determine the difference between those who heard the nonreassuring conclusions and those who heard the reassuring conclusions.

	Nonreassuring	Reassuring	Difference
Item 13			
Item 14			

These scores indicate which subjects experienced the highest degree of anxiety.

c. Total the speaker evaluation scores (seven items), and record the scores according to those who heard the nonreassuring conclusions and those who heard the reassuring conclusions.

	Nonreassuring	Reassuring	Difference
Item 1			
Item 2			
Item 3			
Item 4			
Item 5			
Item 6			
Item 7			

These scores indicate which group of subjects was most impressed by the speaker.

Results

1. Which speech (nonreassuring or reassuring) produced the greatest amount of opinion change?

2. Which group of subjects (those exposed to nonreassuring or reassuring speech) expressed the largest amount of anxiety (worry about nuclear attack and concern about fallout)?

3. Which group of subjects (nonreassuring or reassuring) rated the speech more favorably? On which factors?

Explanation

1. Write a concise summary of this experiment and the results obtained.

2. What advice would you give a speaker about the use of high fear appeals in a speech designed to produce recall of information?

3. Do the data from this study support the assumption that a speech with reassuring recommendations can produce greater shifts of opinions than one with non-reassuring appeals? Why?

4. In order to increase the likelihood of a speaker's receiving a favorable rating from an audience, should he or she use nonreassuring appeals or more reassuring recommendations?

Survey of Attitudes 1

A poll is being taken to determine what students today think about various issues currently being discussed on a local, state, and national level. Would you please check the number on each of the following scales that *best* represents your attitude toward each of the issues.

1. All citizens, both male and female, should be expected to give two years of their lives in service to their country (in military, Peace Corps, etc.).

Strongly Agree ___ : ___ : ___ : ___ : ___ : ___ : ___ Strongly Disagree
                 1   2   3   4   5   6   7

2. Abortion, within three months following conception, should be legalized, regardless of the circumstances under which it is sought.

Strongly Agree ___ : ___ : ___ : ___ : ___ : ___ : ___ Strongly Disagree
                 1   2   3   4   5   6   7

3. Every person should reach legal majority at age 18 (privilege now granted at 21).

Strongly Agree ___ : ___ : ___ : ___ : ___ : ___ : ___ Strongly Disagree
                 1   2   3   4   5   6   7

4. University students should be assessed money to build, equip, and maintain fallout shelters to accommodate the entire student body.

Strongly Agree ___ : ___ : ___ : ___ : ___ : ___ : ___ Strongly Disagree
                 1   2   3   4   5   6   7

5. Our students, male or female, should be given freedom of choice regarding residence and personal activities.

Strongly Agree ___ : ___ : ___ : ___ : ___ : ___ : ___ Strongly Disagree
                 1   2   3   4   5   6   7

6. Birth control pills should be made available to all female students by the university health service.

Strongly Agree ___ : ___ : ___ : ___ : ___ : ___ : ___ Strongly Disagree
                 1   2   3   4   5   6   7

7. Personal consumption of marijuana should not be prohibited by law.

Strongly Agree ___ : ___ : ___ : ___ : ___ : ___ : ___ Strongly Disagree
                 1   2   3   4   5   6   7

8. The mass media should be allowed to operate without censorship controls.

Strongly Agree ___ : ___ : ___ : ___ : ___ : ___ : ___ Strongly Disagree
               1   2   3   4   5   6   7

9. All Christian denominations should unite into one church.

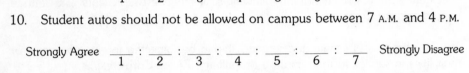

Strongly Agree ___ : ___ : ___ : ___ : ___ : ___ : ___ Strongly Disagree
               1   2   3   4   5   6   7

10. Student autos should not be allowed on campus between 7 A.M. and 4 P.M.

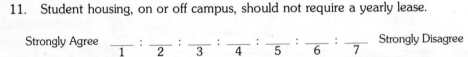

Strongly Agree ___ : ___ : ___ : ___ : ___ : ___ : ___ Strongly Disagree
               1   2   3   4   5   6   7

11. Student housing, on or off campus, should not require a yearly lease.

Strongly Agree ___ : ___ : ___ : ___ : ___ : ___ : ___ Strongly Disagree
               1   2   3   4   5   6   7

12. A conscientious program of sex education should be a part of regular elementary and high school studies.

Strongly Agree ___ : ___ : ___ : ___ : ___ : ___ : ___ Strongly Disagree
               1   2   3   4   5   6   7

Survey of Attitudes 2

A poll is being taken to determine what students today think about various issues currently being discussed on a local, state, and national level. Would you please check the number on each of the following scales that *best* represents your attitude toward each of the issues.

1. All citizens, both male and female, should be expected to give two years of their lives in service to their country (in military, Peace Corps, etc.)

Strongly Agree ___ : ___ : ___ : ___ : ___ : ___ : ___ Strongly Disagree
              1   2   3   4   5   6   7

2. Abortion, within three months following conception, should be legalized, regardless of the circumstances under which it is sought.

Strongly Agree ___ : ___ : ___ : ___ : ___ : ___ : ___ Strongly Disagree
              1   2   3   4   5   6   7

3. Every person should reach legal majority at age 18 (privilege now granted at 21).

Strongly Agree ___ : ___ : ___ : ___ : ___ : ___ : ___ Strongly Disagree
              1   2   3   4   5   6   7

4. University students should be assessed money to build, equip, and maintain fallout shelters to accommodate the entire student body.

Strongly Agree ___ : ___ : ___ : ___ : ___ : ___ : ___ Strongly Disagree
              1   2   3   4   5   6   7

5. Our students, male or female, should be given freedom of choice regarding residence and personal activities.

Strongly Agree ___ : ___ : ___ : ___ : ___ : ___ : ___ Strongly Disagree
              1   2   3   4   5   6   7

6. Birth control pills should be made available to all female students by the university health service.

Strongly Agree ___ : ___ : ___ : ___ : ___ : ___ : ___ Strongly Disagree
              1   2   3   4   5   6   7

7. Personal consumption of marijuana should not be prohibited by law.

Strongly Agree ___ : ___ : ___ : ___ : ___ : ___ : ___ Strongly Disagree
              1   2   3   4   5   6   7

8. The mass media should be allowed to operate without censorship controls.

Strongly Agree $\dfrac{\quad}{1}$: $\dfrac{\quad}{2}$: $\dfrac{\quad}{3}$: $\dfrac{\quad}{4}$: $\dfrac{\quad}{5}$: $\dfrac{\quad}{6}$: $\dfrac{\quad}{7}$ Strongly Disagree

9. All Christian denominations should unite into one church.

Strongly Agree $\dfrac{\quad}{1}$: $\dfrac{\quad}{2}$: $\dfrac{\quad}{3}$: $\dfrac{\quad}{4}$: $\dfrac{\quad}{5}$: $\dfrac{\quad}{6}$: $\dfrac{\quad}{7}$ Strongly Disagree

10. Student autos should not be allowed on campus between 7 A.M. and 4 P.M.

Strongly Agree $\dfrac{\quad}{1}$: $\dfrac{\quad}{2}$: $\dfrac{\quad}{3}$: $\dfrac{\quad}{4}$: $\dfrac{\quad}{5}$: $\dfrac{\quad}{6}$: $\dfrac{\quad}{7}$ Strongly Disagree

11. Student housing, on or off campus, should not require a yearly lease.

Strongly Agree $\dfrac{\quad}{1}$: $\dfrac{\quad}{2}$: $\dfrac{\quad}{3}$: $\dfrac{\quad}{4}$: $\dfrac{\quad}{5}$: $\dfrac{\quad}{6}$: $\dfrac{\quad}{7}$ Strongly Disagree

12. A conscientious program of sex education should be a part of regular elementary and high school studies.

Strongly Agree $\dfrac{\quad}{1}$: $\dfrac{\quad}{2}$: $\dfrac{\quad}{3}$: $\dfrac{\quad}{4}$: $\dfrac{\quad}{5}$: $\dfrac{\quad}{6}$: $\dfrac{\quad}{7}$ Strongly Disagree

13. I feel worried because of what I now know about the threat of nuclear attack.

Extremely Worried $\dfrac{\quad}{1}$: $\dfrac{\quad}{2}$: $\dfrac{\quad}{3}$: $\dfrac{\quad}{4}$: $\dfrac{\quad}{5}$: $\dfrac{\quad}{6}$: $\dfrac{\quad}{7}$ Not at All Worried

14. I am concerned about the dangers of nuclear fallout.

Highly Concerned $\dfrac{\quad}{1}$: $\dfrac{\quad}{2}$: $\dfrac{\quad}{3}$: $\dfrac{\quad}{4}$: $\dfrac{\quad}{5}$: $\dfrac{\quad}{6}$: $\dfrac{\quad}{7}$ Not at All Concerned

Speaker Evaluation Form

1. Was the evidence in the speech satisfactory?

Very
Satisfactory
___ : ___ : ___ : ___ : ___ : ___ : ___
1   2   3   4   5   6   7
Very
Unsatisfactory

2. Do you think the speaker gave a fair presentation of the subject?

Very Fair
___ : ___ : ___ : ___ : ___ : ___ : ___
1   2   3   4   5   6   7
Very Unfair

3. Do you think the speaker was competent to speak on this subject?

Very
Competent
___ : ___ : ___ : ___ : ___ : ___ : ___
1   2   3   4   5   6   7
Very
Incompetent

4. Were the speaker's conclusions justified by the facts?

Completely
Justified
___ : ___ : ___ : ___ : ___ : ___ : ___
1   2   3   4   5   6   7
Completely
Unjustified

5. The speech was:

Very
One-Sided
___ : ___ : ___ : ___ : ___ : ___ : ___
1   2   3   4   5   6   7
Very
Two-Sided

6. The speech was:

Very Logical
___ : ___ : ___ : ___ : ___ : ___ : ___
1   2   3   4   5   6   7
Very Emotional

7. The speaker seemed to be a likable person.

Very
Likable
___ : ___ : ___ : ___ : ___ : ___ : ___
1   2   3   4   5   6   7
Very
Unlikable

117

Speech Text

At 8:13 A.M. on August 6, 1945, the *Enola Gay* was circling the city of Hiroshima. At 8:14 the target was sighted, and at 8:15 the first nuclear bomb in the history of the world was dropped. First came the "pika" (the flash), and in that instant over 62,000 men, women, and children died. Then came the blast, and an additional 8,000 were killed. Then came the mushroom cloud, and the "living dead" were crying for water, and their faces were like rubber and dropped off of their bodies like masks. Their skin fell off like shredded cloth. The total killed was 78,000. And three days later, on August 9, at 11:02 A.M. in Nagasaki, 74,000 died in the streets. The total killed just by two bombs—152,000.

Today you can visit Peace Park in Hiroshima. It is located at ground zero, the hypocenter. There is a museum there that has display cases showing remnants from a lost civilization—watches stopped at 8:15, twisted iron gratings, and granite steps with shadowed patterns across the surface. These shadowed patterns are the outlines of victims whose bodies shielded the spot against the atomic flash which lightened the rest of the stone. An article in *Life,* 1965, described Hiroshima: "In the instant of detonation 70,000 people were cremated in their tracks, thousands of others suffered radiation that was to prove fatal, and the city was obliterated." John Hersey's book *Hiroshima,* 1964, is an account of 6 people who survived the blast. In the account, one survivor said, "eyes ran from sockets, flesh bubbled from the bone, and the city disappeared in a flash."

This act—which had taken years to perfect—made the United States the first and leading member of the nuclear powers. Only 5 short years later Russia became a full-fledged member. In 1952 Great Britain joined. In 1960 France became the fourth member. And in 1964 China joined the group. And today, there are more likely members of this once powerful, select group—India, Israel, Egypt, West Germany, Canada, Sweden, South Africa, and even Japan. This is an impressive list, you may say. But surely not one of these nations would seriously consider using a nuclear weapon? However, since 1945 the United States or Russia has seriously contemplated using nuclear weapons on at least five occasions:

1. In 1954 to release the French Garrison of Dien-bien-phu.

2. In 1956 in the Suez crisis when Prime Minister Khrushchev threatened rocket retaliation on French and British forces.

3. In 1958 in Lebanon when the United States landed troops to prevent a Communist takeover.

4. In 1958 during the Quemoy crisis.

5. During John F. Kennedy's administration the greatest nuclear confrontation—the Cuban missile crisis—occurred.

Perhaps the gravest and greatest problem of nuclear weapons is the spread of these weapons to smaller nations. Dr. Jerome Wiesner, formerly President Kennedy's science advisor, estimated in 1963 that in two decades, as many as 20 nations may have nuclear arms. And Senator Robert F. Kennedy "has raised the specter of the big powers being drawn into conflict because of the irresponsible action of the little one-bomb nations." It is just like letting a bunch of little kids play with loaded guns. Eventually one of them will shoot somebody. So it is not the large, responsible nations that we need to worry about, but some of these countries whose behavior seems irrational and irresponsible. Take China for instance.

On October 19, 1964, China exploded her first bomb. Eight months later—in June 1965—China exploded her second bomb.

What the Chinese did was to "leapfrog" some of the tedious steps the United States took to produce its first bombs. The Chinese have reaped the benefits of America's and Russia's findings. "Many of our officials believe that a lot of classified information was given to the Chinese by three traitors, and in 1950 the Russians collaborated with Mao's technicians." A 1965 *Life* article states that by the 1970s China could produce a 100-megaton hydrogen bomb. Dr. Ralph E. Lapp, nuclear physicist, who worked on the first A-bomb project in Chicago, states: "It is a risky state of mind which would dismiss China, out of hand, as a primitive two-bomb country. China can, in a very few years, become the most dangerous nuclear power of all—not because the Chinese leaders can match the U.S. might, but because they do not seem to understand what a nuclear war could do, and therefore, they might not be rationally deterred from starting one." Again, all of us would agree that nuclear war is irrational, but China does not operate from the same rational base that we do. A *Newsweek* article quoted General Lo Qui-Ching, Peking's Army Chief of Staff as saying, "It is the time for the Chinese to make realistic preparation for nuclear war so that, come what may, we shall be in a position to cope with the situation successfully." He added that while a nuclear war will "cause sacrifices and destruction, it will also educate the people."

The attitude of General Lo and Mao and others in China is typical. These men believe that their country could survive a nuclear attack. Therefore, a conflict that to us is unthinkable is, to them, quite reasonable. In 1963 Mao and Khrushchev met and publicly quarreled over a nuclear test ban. According to Khrushchev, Mao said, "Can one guess how great will be the toll of human casualties in a future war? Possibly it would be a third of the 2.7 billion inhabitants of the entire world." "But even if half of the world's humanity were destroyed," he added, "the other half would still remain, but imperialism would be destroyed entirely and there would be only socialism in all the world, and within half a century, the population would again increase by more than half."

Let's look at some of the facts which support or explain Chinese reasoning.

Fact 1: China is the most populous nation on the earth (720 million). By 1984 there will likely be one billion Chinese in China. In 1957 before China even had the bomb, Mao said, "We aren't afraid of the bomb. What if it did kill 300 million Chinese? We would still have plenty more. China would be the last country to die."

Fact 2: Only one-seventh of China's population is in the cities. Mao might think that his people are dispersed enough so that large numbers of them would not be killed at one time.

Fact 3: China is on a low rung of the economic ladder. Therefore, in case of nuclear war, China might have a positive advantage: "China has less to lose." This is how China thinks, and this is why China is not afraid of nuclear war.

In late 1964 Mao told Edgar Snow, a U.S. correspondent, that he had been reading the U.S. reports on the follow-up studies on Bikini Atoll in the Pacific where the U.S. Atomic Energy Commission tested many nuclear weapons in the 40s and 50s. Mao noted that wildlife and vegetation had been seen on the islands. He has deduced that fallout must not be too bad; animals and people are still living. Part of the blame for this attitude can be placed on the many U.S. scientists who played down fallout in their early zeal to continue nuclear testing. By this, we have, in part, defeated our own purpose—that of deterring a nuclear attack, by playing down the potency of our own weapon.

Well, what does all of this mean to us? It means first that all of the authorities writing on this subject agree on one thing: *There will be a nuclear confrontation.* It is not a question of *if* but a question of *when.* And this is not the position of some fly-by-night alarmist; it is simply a cold, hard fact, and it is time we wake up and face facts no matter how unpleasant they might be.

After the Cuban Missile Crisis, a lot of calculation was done to determine how many Americans would have died *if* the attack had come. Don Oberdorfer, writing for the *Saturday Evening Post* in March 1963, reports that a "moderate-sized" attack would have killed 13 million Americans outright.

This same author presented the findings of Operation Spade Fork, another study designed to calculate what would happen if the buttons were pushed and nuclear warheads fell on the continental United States. This operation assumed 355 nuclear weapons ranging in size from 1 to 10 megatons were dropped on the U.S.—186 air-burst and rest ground-burst. The total explosive power of this would be 1,799 megatons—equivalent to one billion seven hundred ninety-nine million tons of TNT. Here are the calculations: 13 million Americans would be killed instantly, and 8 million more would die as a result of fire, burns, and blast injuries; 13 million more would be killed by radioactive fallout. This is a total of 34 million people.

Conclusion: Nonreasurring

Obviously, it is time for all of us to accept the rather harsh fact that things will not always be as pleasant and peaceful as they are now. It is time for us, at the very least, to prepare ourselves mentally for this impending confrontation.

Conclusion: Reassuring

Must we just sit around and wait for all of this to happen? Do we have to be among these 34 million people? The answer is a resounding NO. In the first place, [name of university] is not a prime target. We may like [name of university], and it may be a pretty good school, but no one seems to be particularly interested in dropping bombs on it. Therefore, we would not be among the 21 million people killed as a result of either a direct or near hit. However, we would certainly be prime candidates to be among the 13 million who would die from fallout poisoning. Why? *[Here at Auburn University we are 30 miles from Columbus, Georgia. This is the home of the largest infantry training center in the world. Other distances that would affect us are: Atlanta, 110 miles; Huntsville, 220 miles; Birmingham, 135 miles; Montgomery, 60 miles; and Mobile is 220 miles. That puts Auburn in what is called the Remote and Fringe Area in case of nuclear attack. If a bomb were dropped in Columbus, Georgia, fallout would reach us in 10 minutes to one hour,] depending on atmospheric conditions and prevailing winds. If we had no protection, underground protection, all of us would die in one hour or so. If we had good, underground protection, all of us would live. Here at [name of university], as you know, there are basements of buildings that are designated as fallout shelters, but these will not be effective enough. First, fire is likely, and, secondly, there is a possibility of collapse; for example, [name of a campus building] is a designated area. And, thirdly, and most important, the most effective, accessible thing that will protect you against fallout is dirt. There must be dirt on all sides of us and above our heads if we are to live through this thing.

Now before you dismiss this as another fallout shelter pitch, listen to a few facts about nuclear war and living through it.

You and I are not going to be able to make the choice between peace and war. It has already been demonstrated how easily this war could be started. Since the decision will not be ours to make, there is only one sensible thing for us to do: Prepare ourselves for a nuclear war, for by all accounts, it IS coming. It is only a matter of when.

Everyone in Hiroshima and Nagasaki was not killed by the bombs. As you know, Japan had been warned that the bombs would be dropped. Both of these cities had shelter provisions. In both cities this is a true and proven conclusion: The people inside the shelters were virtually unharmed (except for minor bruises and scratches), and the people outside the shelters were killed. And many of these shelters consisted of "excavations supported only by beams and roofed with wood and earth." The things that you and I know as storm shelters were these fallout shelters. These shelters withstood the blast even at 300 yards. Nagasaki had tunnel-type shelters that would have accommodated 75,000 people. The air-raid warning was sounded; the people thought it was only a routine warning, and only 400 were in the shelters. Everyone outside the shelters was killed.

This is the best argument that I have been able to find in favor of building shelters: *They will keep you and me alive in a nuclear attack.* Shelters in the

*Adapt the portions of the text between brackets to your specific locale by inserting appropriate local information.

United States could save 90% of the lives of those who would otherwise die. But to be fair, we should look at some of the anti-shelter arguments.

1. No shelter could protect me against a direct hit. This is true, but a simple elementary calculation shows that 99% of the area of the United States is not in the region of total destruction. And [name of university] certainly isn't.

2. Even if the shelter saved me, the fires will kill me. This is a good argument against poorly constructed shelters. If the shelter is properly constructed, fire will not burn you to death.

3. Life would not be worth living if nuclear war came. Certainly things wouldn't be luxurious. But this country has enough surplus food to feed us for a long time to come, and "It would be arrogant to deny future generations the privilege of living as good a life as they can make for themselves."

4. Better to work for peace than build shelters. We should do both. We MUST be prepared, and that includes war preparation. It is the foolish person who does not consider the alternatives. So there is no really sound argument against building fallout shelters.

As a result of all the evidence we have found, we are suggesting, even urging, that adequate fallout shelters be provided for the [name of university] campus.

A shelter for a fringe area like [name of university] that would protect us against fire and fallout would cost between $80.00 and $140.00 per person. This type can be built in 4 months. Does $140.00 sound like a lot? It is 560 cans of beer at 35 cents per can or 100 late-late movies at the War Eagle. Or it is $11.66 per quarter for 12 quarters. We are asking that all [name of university] students get behind the move to provide these shelters. We have prepared a petition urging the immediate consideration of this proposal. In this petition we are showing the "powers that be" that we are interested enough to pay our fair share toward the construction. We state that we are willing to assess ourselves to the tune of $11.66 per quarter (that's about 16 cents per day) to provide us this protection.

I think that not only at [name of university] but at all universities and colleges this must be done. Obviously, we must preserve as many people as possible, but particularly our educated young. Someone must be around to take the reins and provide the leadership that will be needed. Because of large concentrations of highly intelligent people in a university, it is doubly or triply important to provide maximum protection. The future looks bleak because of this eminent threat, but it looks impossible if you lost your intelligent youth. So please sign this petition and show that we are mature enough and interested enough to prepare for our future whatever it may be.

Part 3
Experiments about Information Diffusion

Part 3

Chapter 5
Face-to-Face Groups

The lecture, an informative speech, is widely used in all kinds of educational settings—high school and university classes and industrial training sessions—to disseminate information to groups of people. The informative speech has survived as a method of securing understanding because of its adaptability to individual differences and circumstances. The informative speaker can interpret, respond directly to, guide, and amplify aspects of a message that seem unclear to an audience. The lecturer may also motivate the listeners through enthusiasm and personal modes of presenting materials. The experiments that follow represent ways of testing the efficacy of diffusing information to audiences by means of speeches and lectures.

The great tradition of rhetoric and public speaking are inextricably woven into the background that surrounds any discussion of transmitting information to an audience by means of oral presentation. The speech whose purpose is to inform is the one most commonly taught in introductory speech courses. The experiments that follow test how effectively an audience is able to obtain information transmitted by speeches.

Experiment 5.1
Oral Lecture vs. Manuscript

Proposition
Lecturing can be an effective method of diffusing information to a large, face-to-face group.

Research Question
Is a speech presented to a face-to-face audience more effective in terms of information retention and attitude change than the same presentation given over a loudspeaker without the speaker present or when read as a manuscript?

Research Methods*

Subjects
Sixty individuals of approximately the same age and class standing who will be divided into 3 groups of 20 each.

One person who will memorize the speech and present it to an audience.

Materials
Cover sheets for pre- and postadministration of the Opinion Poll (60 copies each).

Opinion Poll (120 copies).

Speech on Wealth.

Three rooms: one with a microphone (the face-to-face room), one with a loud-speaker connected to the microphone, and a third room in the vicinity (the manuscript room).

Procedures
1. Selection and Preparation of Subjects
   a. Approximately two weeks before the experiment, administer the Opinion Poll on the topic of the speech to the 60 subjects.
   b. On the day of the experiment, arrange to have all 60 subjects arrive at the room with the microphone that will carry the speech to the adjoining room by means of the loudspeaker.
   c. Then assign 20 subjects to the face-to-face room, 20 subjects to the loud-speaker room, and 20 subjects to the manuscript room.
2. Conduct of the Experiment
   a. Make certain that the microphone is live and broadcasting to the loud-speaker room.
   b. Introduce the speaker to the face-to-face audience (with the loudspeaker audience listening).
   c. Simultaneously with the introduction of the speaker, distribute to each member in the manuscript audience a copy of the speech.
   d. Allow the manuscript audience to read the speech for the same period of time that the speaker is talking; collect the manuscripts at the end of the time period.
   e. Administer the Opinion Poll again to all three audiences.
   f. Collect the polls and debrief the audiences.
3. Tabulation of the Data
   Record the mean Opinion Poll scores for each of the three groups.

---

*Adapted from an experiment reported in Walter H. Wilke, "An Experimental Comparison of the Speech, the Radio, and the Printed Page as Propaganda Devices," *Archives of Psychology,* No. 169 (June 1934), pp. 5–32.

Subject	Mean Scale Scores for Each Group Member								
	Live			Loudspeaker			Manuscript		
	Pre	Post	Shift	Pre	Post	Shift	Pre	Post	Shift
1									
2									
3									
4									
5									
6									
7									
8									
9									
10									
11									
12									
13									
14									
15									
16									
17									
18									
19									
20									

Name _____   Section _____

Date _____   Instructor _____

Results

1. What percentage of the subjects in each group shifted mean scores on the attitude scales?

2. Which method (live speech, loudspeaker, manuscript) produced the greatest change according to the scale scores?

Explanation

1. Write a concise summary of this experiment and the results obtained.

2. What support do the results of this study provide for the research question?

3. Based on the results of this study, what advice would you give to a student group that wants to inform a student body about its purpose?

Cover Sheet for Prespeech Administration

Please indicate your opinion on each of the accompanying statements by checking the number that best describes your view. For example, if you agree heartily with the following statement, you would indicate your agreement as shown: *All final examinations should be abolished.*

Strongly ✔ : ___ : ___ : ___ : ___ : ___ : ___ Strongly
Approve 1   2   3   4   5   6   7   Disapprove

I agree to indicate on this ballot my frank and honest opinions. It is understood, of course, that these opinions are to be held strictly confidential.

Cover Sheet for Postspeech Administration

A while back you were kind enough to indicate your opinions on the same subject as the speech you have just heard. We would like to have you indicate your opinions once more because we wish to see if opinions change or fluctuate over a short period of time.

As before, the opinions you indicate will be held strictly confidential. Mark the ballot by checking the number that best describes your opinion. *Be sure to answer every question.*

Opinion Poll

1. We should oppose the more equal distribution of wealth since it is likely to stifle individual initiative.

Strongly Approve ___:___:___:___:___:___:___ Strongly Disapprove
  1   2   3   4   5   6   7

2. It would be far better for the country if great fortunes were not allowed to accumulate.

Strongly Approve ___:___:___:___:___:___:___ Strongly Disapprove
  1   2   3   4   5   6   7

3. Inheritance taxes should confiscate the bulk of all large private fortunes.

Strongly Approve ___:___:___:___:___:___:___ Strongly Disapprove
  1   2   3   4   5   6   7

4. Income taxes should be so high in the upper brackets that the great portion of the larger incomes is confiscated.

Strongly Approve ___:___:___:___:___:___:___ Strongly Disapprove
  1   2   3   4   5   6   7

5. It is contrary to the interests of the people of the United States to permit the concentration of wealth in the hands of a few people.

Strongly Approve ___:___:___:___:___:___:___ Strongly Disapprove
  1   2   3   4   5   6   7

6. Since only a few people are capable of handling the complex problems of large-scale industries, the wealth of this country is rightfully placed largely in their hands.

Strongly Approve ___:___:___:___:___:___:___ Strongly Disapprove
  1   2   3   4   5   6   7

7. It is socially undesirable for the children of the very rich to inherit the huge fortunes of their parents.

Strongly Approve ___:___:___:___:___:___:___ Strongly Disapprove
  1   2   3   4   5   6   7

8. We should encourage the development of big fortunes as vitally necessary to supply large amounts of capital for our huge business and financial enterprises.

Strongly Approve ___:___:___:___:___:___:___ Strongly Disapprove
  1   2   3   4   5   6   7

9. The colossal need for relief at the same time as an oversupply of food and other necessities shows that the ownership of wealth should be redistributed.

Strongly Approve ___:___:___:___:___:___:___ Strongly Disapprove
  1   2   3   4   5   6   7

10. The enormous wealth of the extremely rich should be more uniformly distributed among all the people.

Strongly Approve ___:___:___:___:___:___:___ Strongly Disapprove
  1   2   3   4   5   6   7

11. In gauging a nation's prosperity and wealth, one should form his or her judgment on the basis of the greatest fortunes attained in that nation.

Strongly
Approve $\overline{\quad 1 \quad}$: $\overline{\quad 2 \quad}$: $\overline{\quad 3 \quad}$: $\overline{\quad 4 \quad}$: $\overline{\quad 5 \quad}$: $\overline{\quad 6 \quad}$: $\overline{\quad 7 \quad}$ Strongly Disapprove

12. The wealth of this country is now distributed approximately as it should be.

Strongly
Approve $\overline{\quad 1 \quad}$: $\overline{\quad 2 \quad}$: $\overline{\quad 3 \quad}$: $\overline{\quad 4 \quad}$: $\overline{\quad 5 \quad}$: $\overline{\quad 6 \quad}$: $\overline{\quad 7 \quad}$ Strongly Disapprove

13. Most of our wealthy people do not deserve the huge fortunes they have accumulated.

Strongly
Approve $\overline{\quad 1 \quad}$: $\overline{\quad 2 \quad}$: $\overline{\quad 3 \quad}$: $\overline{\quad 4 \quad}$: $\overline{\quad 5 \quad}$: $\overline{\quad 6 \quad}$: $\overline{\quad 7 \quad}$ Strongly Disapprove

14. Individual thrift and initiative should not be dampened by any limitation or taxation of hereditary wealth.

Strongly
Approve $\overline{\quad 1 \quad}$: $\overline{\quad 2 \quad}$: $\overline{\quad 3 \quad}$: $\overline{\quad 4 \quad}$: $\overline{\quad 5 \quad}$: $\overline{\quad 6 \quad}$: $\overline{\quad 7 \quad}$ Strongly Disapprove

15. The wealthiest people in the United States have amply justified the existence of great fortunes by their generous gifts to science and charity.

Strongly
Approve $\overline{\quad 1 \quad}$: $\overline{\quad 2 \quad}$: $\overline{\quad 3 \quad}$: $\overline{\quad 4 \quad}$: $\overline{\quad 5 \quad}$: $\overline{\quad 6 \quad}$: $\overline{\quad 7 \quad}$ Strongly Disapprove

16. There should be no restriction except one's own ability upon the amount of money one may honestly acquire.

Strongly
Approve $\overline{\quad 1 \quad}$: $\overline{\quad 2 \quad}$: $\overline{\quad 3 \quad}$: $\overline{\quad 4 \quad}$: $\overline{\quad 5 \quad}$: $\overline{\quad 6 \quad}$: $\overline{\quad 7 \quad}$ Strongly Disapprove

17. Our government should get at the real basis of depressions by taxing the wealthy sufficiently to give the masses of people enough to purchase what they need.

Strongly
Approve $\overline{\quad 1 \quad}$: $\overline{\quad 2 \quad}$: $\overline{\quad 3 \quad}$: $\overline{\quad 4 \quad}$: $\overline{\quad 5 \quad}$: $\overline{\quad 6 \quad}$: $\overline{\quad 7 \quad}$ Strongly Disapprove

18. The wealthy are already doing more than their share in paying heavy taxes.

Strongly
Approve $\overline{\quad 1 \quad}$: $\overline{\quad 2 \quad}$: $\overline{\quad 3 \quad}$: $\overline{\quad 4 \quad}$: $\overline{\quad 5 \quad}$: $\overline{\quad 6 \quad}$: $\overline{\quad 7 \quad}$ Strongly Disapprove

19. The government ought to make it impossible for individuals to acquire such huge fortunes as are now in existence.

Strongly
Approve $\overline{\quad 1 \quad}$: $\overline{\quad 2 \quad}$: $\overline{\quad 3 \quad}$: $\overline{\quad 4 \quad}$: $\overline{\quad 5 \quad}$: $\overline{\quad 6 \quad}$: $\overline{\quad 7 \quad}$ Strongly Disapprove

20. Money or property must be held inviolate and immune to seizure by governments, even in times of war, famine, or national stress.

Strongly
Approve $\overline{\quad 1 \quad}$: $\overline{\quad 2 \quad}$: $\overline{\quad 3 \quad}$: $\overline{\quad 4 \quad}$: $\overline{\quad 5 \quad}$: $\overline{\quad 6 \quad}$: $\overline{\quad 7 \quad}$ Strongly Disapprove

Speech on Wealth*

James Thurber, in his book *The Dog That Bites*, writes how his mother often apologized for the misbehavior of Muggs, the family dog, attributing it to the fact that the dog was not well. "He may not have been well," Thurber observes, "but he is indeed terribly strong." Mr. Thurber has unknowingly but yet very clearly illustrated a poignant economic condition that exists in the United States. There has been a strong movement in the past several years toward the socialistic concept of the equalization of wealth within our society.

One of the most recent and most visible examples of this trend occurred in the 1972 California Presidential Primary where Senator George McGovern captured the hearts and votes of the middle class and poor electorate with the promise of giving every American family within prescribed poverty standards an outright gift of $1,000 per year. Hidden within the depths of the financing mechanisms he outlined for the funding of this program lay an ominous evil in the form of increased taxes upon the wealthy. He said, in essence, that our government should get at the real basis of depression by taxing the wealthy sufficiently to give the masses of people enough to purchase what they need. He seemed to be supporting the economic philosophy that income taxes should be so high in the upper brackets that the greater portion of the larger incomes be confiscated. This modern day Robin Hood quickly abandoned this philosophy but unfortunately not before the majority of the American people were able to show their disapproval.

Such a cure-all economic plan has not been seen in this country since John Maynard Keynes descended from the right hand of the almighty in the 1930s to lead this nation out of the clutches of the depression and into economic bliss. This plan purports that the enormous wealth of the very rich should be more uniformly distributed among all the people. The idea of the equalization of wealth will obviously create a massive disincentive for work and economic progress. We should oppose the more even distribution of wealth since it is likely to stifle individual initiative. There should be no restrictions on an individual's earning power except his own ability upon the amount of money he may honestly acquire. A good number of misconceptions which give support to the equalization-of-wealth concept are based upon the incorrect and dangerous premise that most of our wealthy people do not deserve the huge fortunes which they have accumulated. This idea assumes a Marxist position that all profits are bad. These people may often even go so far as to associate evil dealings with the accumulation of wealth.

It is unfortunate that so many otherwise rational people are misled into believing that the usurpation of one man's wealth will somehow improve his own economic condition. The apostles of this theory preach that it would be far better for the country if great fortunes were not allowed to accumulate. They support this position with the philosophical stand that it is contrary to the interests of the people of the United States to permit the concentration of wealth in the hands of a few people.

On the surface, it is very appealing to the American Dream to have equality among all people. The truth of the matter is that the reason that the American

---

*Original speech by Charles Mac Haddow, a student at Brigham Young University. By permission.

Dream even exists is the basic integrity of this nation's economic institutions. The capitalistic foundations of this government demand that we should encourage the development of big fortunes as vitally necessary to supply large amounts of capital for our huge business and financial enterprises. This concentration of wealth allows for necessary, directed decision-making powers that would be impossible if the necessary resources were too diverse to be utilized effectively. A popular notion is that since a few people are capable of handling the complex problems of large-scale industries, the wealth of this country is rightfully placed largely in their hands. This is a prostitution of the idea of the value of concentrated capital. The powers of directed decision making and the effective utilization of resources are far more important than the actual number of people involved. This misconception has its roots in the absurd notion that in gauging a nation's prosperity and wealth, one should form his judgment on the basis of the greatest fortunes attained in that nation. Many great fortunes have been accumulated in every economy at the expense of the poor people. Our system gives viable alternatives to such abuses within our economic system.

Careful introspection of our economy shows clearly that a man can become wealthy within the framework of a free capitalistic marketplace. It has been suggested that a glaring inequity exists in the ability of a man to pass along his riches to his children who have done little or nothing to warrant the increase. If we accept the premise that there is some value to operating within an open marketplace, we somehow taint the foundations of the system when we allow wealth to flow into the uncalloused hands of naive children. It is socially undesirable that the children of the very rich should inherit the huge fortunes of their parents. We then must ask ourselves the question of whether there are proper remedies that can be implemented. Some might suggest that inheritance taxes should confiscate the bulk of all large private fortunes. This idea assumes that the government is a better keeper of the money than the free marketplace and as such is unacceptable to us as an alternative. The damage that might be done by a child in this circumstance seems minimal when you weigh the disadvantages of this system to the proper concept that individual thrift and initiative should not be dampened by any limitation or taxation of inherited wealth.

Actually, it is the control of the wealth that is the primary concern here. Some have argued that the wealthiest people in the United States have amply justified the existence of great fortunes by their generous gifts to science and charity. They tell us further that the wealthy are already doing more than their share in paying heavy taxes. Meanwhile, those who have a penchant for applying economic solutions to social problems argue that the colossal need for relief in the face of an oversupply of food and other necessities shows that ownership of wealth should be redistributed. Considering the nature of our economic system and its attendant institutions, it appears that the wealth of this country is now distributed approximately as it should be, with some minor tax reforms necessitated with periodic changes of economic conditions. It is clear, however, that the very basis for the continued existence of the capitalistic economy has its roots in the basic axiom that money or property must be held inviolate and immune to seizure by governments, even in times of war, famine, or national stress.

Experiment 5.2
Seeing vs. Hearing a Speaker

Proposition
Lecturing is more likely to be effective when the speaker can be seen than when he or she is not present.

Research Questions
Is there a difference in listening ability between audiences when one group sees and hears the speaker and the other only hears the speaker?

Is the element of visual cues in a face-to-face situation an aid to the understanding and retention of expository material?

Research Methods*

Subjects
One hundred individuals assembled in an auditorium or small theater such as a theater-in-the-round that can be divided by a heavy curtain.

One speaker.

Materials
A memorized lecture on New Zealand to be presented in an extemporaneous manner.

A multiple-choice Listening Test (100 copies).

Speaker's stand with microphone and 2 loudspeakers.

Procedures
1. Selection and Preparation of Subjects
   a. Arrange for a group of 100 subjects to hear a lecture in a little theater (preferably a theater-in-the-round), where a heavy curtain divides them into 2 groups of at least 50 each.
   b. Place a podium on the right side of the lecture room so that the group seated on the right may both see and hear the speaker. Place a loudspeaker on each side of the lecture room. The subjects on the left side of the room will only hear the speaker.
2. Conduct of the Experiment
   a. As soon as the subjects are seated and the experimental situation is arranged, introduce the speaker. Indicate that a test will be administered on the content of the speech immediately following its conclusion.

*Adapted from an experiment reported in Edward J. J. Kramar and Thomas R. Lewis, "Comparison of Visual and Nonvisual Listening," *Journal of Communication*, Vol. 1 (Nov. 1951), pp. 16–20. By permission.

b. Have the speaker present the speech.
c. Following the speech, distribute the tests.
d. Collect the tests and answer sheets, and debrief the subjects.
3. Tabulation of the Data
    a. Score the answer sheets, and record the scores for each subject in each condition.

Subject	No. of Correct Answers	
	See–Hear	Hear Only
1		
2		
3		
4		
5		
6		
7		
8		
9		
10		

Add other sheets.

b. Calculate the mean scores for the 2 experimental groups (see and hear vs. hear only).

Mean No. of Correct Answers	
See–Hear	Hear Only

Results

1. Which group of subjects scored higher on the test?

2. Does the presence of a live speaker tend to contribute to the ability of a listener to remember ideas in a speech?

3. Could anything else have accounted for the difference between the two groups of subjects?

Explanation

1. Write a concise summary of this experiment and the results obtained.

2. Do the results of this study provide an answer to the research questions? In what way?

3. What advice would you give a speaker, based on the results of this study?

Lecture: New Zealand

In the summer of 1941, two men seated side by side on a train began a conversation. They were riding over the pleasant rolling countryside of Wisconsin, and, quite naturally, they began talking about the rural scenes they saw from the train window. One of the men was clearly a farmer, and the other man's occupation was manufacturing. The farmer asked, "What part of the country are you from?" And his friend replied, "Oh, I'm from New Zealand." "New Zealand? Why that's around Australia somewhere, isn't it?" The New Zealander took out his notebook and drew a rough map of the South Pacific to show New Zealand's location, 1,400 miles from Australia and 6,000 miles from South America. "Do you mean that little strip of land with all the water around it?" Why, what do you do when the tide comes in?" the farmer asked.

I use this little episode to illustrate my belief that New Zealand isn't very well known to the people of the United States. I expect that prior to 1940, most of us thought of New Zealand as a tiny strip of land just off the coast of Australia. We may have known a little about some of the wars fought in that area between the English and the natives, but certainly our knowledge about New Zealand was limited. Since World War II, however, our information about this British Dominion has been improved. You see, there were large numbers of American forces stationed in New Zealand during the last war, and our troops came back with many stories about the enjoyable hospitality of the New Zealanders as well as information about this South Pacific country. I happen to have had the opportunity of visiting New Zealand as a member of the armed forces, and this evening I would like to tell you about some of the things I have learned about that country. I think you will be interested in knowing something about the geography, history, government, and economic conditions of this progressive country.

First of all, let me locate and describe the country for you. The Dominion of New Zealand is located southeast of Australia and almost due west of the southern part of South America. It lies in the southern hemisphere, and, therefore, summer extends from December to early March, and winter from June to late August. I remember, when I was there, how strange it felt to be eating in March and April what I had always thought of as late fall fruits. The climate in the southern part of New Zealand is cooler than in the north; however, because of ocean currents the overall range in temperature is very slight. This little country is plentifully supplied with rainfall; and, as a matter of fact, most areas have a yearly total of over thirty-five inches. As in other parts of the South Pacific, fog plays a very minor part in the weather conditions; you would seldom, if ever, see such fogs as frequently occur in the coastal areas of the U.S. The pleasant weather and the diversity of scenery make New Zealand a favorite vacation land for travelers because it it is so easy to get to so many beautiful spots. Travelers can enjoy subtropical forest, volcanoes, hot springs, plopping mud pools, and blue and green tinted lakes, all within an easy day's travel by automobile. There are two very important harbors; both of them are located in North Island; and there are several trade routes which enter these ports. Still New Zealand is isolated somewhat from other countries by a tremendous expanse of ocean. However, in these days of modern air clippers, these distances do not mean as much to us as they did a few years ago.

As we look closer at the country, we notice that it is long and narrow, with its two islands stretching out 1,000 miles, although at no point is either island wider than 280 miles. And, of that total area, a considerable portion of it is rather rough. Someone has said that if New Zealand was rolled out flat, it would be a fine, large country. Instead, nearly two-thirds of the total area has an elevation of between 650 feet and 3,500 feet, and rather less than a quarter is below 650 feet. Of that one-fourth, the proportion of lowland is small because a significant portion of it is rugged and broken. Some of the highest mountains are volcanic even though there has been no eruption since 1886. Since the country is so mountainous, many of its chief lakes are at high altitudes and, therefore, of very little value for transportation. Most of the rivers have little transportation value either because they are short or because they are swift flowing and broken with rapids. The lakes are not completely useless, however, because the qualities that make them of little value for transportation make them a source of hydroelectric power.

In addition to the geographical features of this southern land, I was very much interested in the original inhabitants, the Maoris. These people are called Polynesians, and they are probably of Caucausian origin since the type can be found in all of the islands of the Southern Pacific region. Historians point out that these people made their exploration trips in the outrigger canoe which is common from Ceylon and Malaya throughout the far-flung islands of the Pacific. The speculation is that along about 500 A.D. Hawaii was occupied by the Polynesians, and 400 years later, about 900. A.D., New Zealand was discovered by them, and thus man settled the last territory of the globe. These natives did not have compasses to guide them in their travels, nor did they have a knowledge of mariners' mathematics. They viewed the stars to memorize their movements, and, then, by watching the stars at night and the birds by day, they made their explorations into the vast Pacific Ocean. These Polynesian people were in New Zealand long before the white man set foot there.

It wasn't until 1769 that Captain James Cook, one of England's greatest explorer-navigators, landed on North Island and took possession of New Zealand in the name of King George III. He later circumnavigated South Island and upon his return to England suggested colonization of New Zealand. But because of the discouraging experiences with the American colonies, Great Britain refused to take immediate steps toward colonization. Now, that did not mean that New Zealand went completely untouched by white men. A few years later, a trade route to an Australian convict settlement was established and Auckland, now the capital of New Zealand, became a port of call for masts and spars to equip the sailing vessels. Traders also exchanged liquor and muskets with the Maoris for food, flax, and timber. It was about 1800 that a white settlement was begun. The settlement consisted mostly of avaricious traders, runaway sailors, and escaped convicts; but in 1814 a mission was established to help the Maoris protect themselves against the evils of white civilization. In 1840 colonization was rapidly advancing, and with it war and bloodshed developed. Land-hungry colonists bought some land, but they stole most of it from the Maoris. The Maoris protested loudly that the colonists taught the natives to look up to heaven while their lands were stolen from under their feet. Finally, in 1867, the New Zealand government adopted legislation providing for an end of the conflict, and steps toward stable and lasting partnership between the two races were made. Since that time, great advancement has been made in social relationships between these two groups, and the general conditions of the Maoris have improved. This remarkable racial revival was partly inspired by the slogan "Hold fast to your Maorihood." Inasmuch as we have considered New Zealand's historical development, let's now turn and consider her political development.

Politically speaking, New Zealand is a dominion, but this term in relationship to the British constitution cannot be defined too easily. You see, New Zealand is not a colony even though it began its life as a colony. Perhaps the best definition of the status of New Zealand can be found in the definition proposed by the American Continental Congress of 1776: "All members of the British Empire are distinct states, independent of each other, but connected together under the same sovereign, in right of the same crown." As a result of these ideas, New Zealand is not subject to Great Britain in regard to taxes, war, commercial or tariff policies, but she does have a common allegiance to the "crown" or King.

You may be interested in her governmental affairs since you probably remember reading something about them a short time ago. In case you have forgotten, the people defeated the Labor party at the polls and thus expressed their disfavor with some of the socialistic principles of that party. That action is beside the purpose of my talk, however, because I merely want to describe the broad organization of the government for you. Legislatively, there are two chambers, the Legislative Council or upper house and the House of Representatives or lower house. The upper house is composed of appointed members much like those of England's House of Lords, and they have no power to initiate or amend legislation imposing taxation or affecting revenue in any way. The House of Representatives is the elective body, and the elections are normally held every three years. The executive branch of the government is the Executive Council, or Cabinet. The leader of the elected majority party is sent for by the Governor-general and asked to form a ministry. The leader of the majority party becomes the Prime Minister, and he then chooses the members of the cabinet. In the past, there have been two main political parties organized in the country, the Labor party and the National party. Thus you see the broad organization of the government resembles that of Great Britain more than that of the United States.

Thus far I have described the general location and geography of New Zealand, as well as the early settlement and political organization. I would like now to describe certain economic aspects with which I am familiar. New Zealand, when you get down to it, is primarily a pastoral and agricultural country; she is butter not steel; grass not petroleum. Even though the proportion of people engaged in farming has decreased during the past twenty years, the lack of steel still hinders the advance of manufacturing industries in New Zealand. It is quite true that there are extensive iron ores available in unexplored regions, but exploitation was subdued because of the war. And even though coal is inadequate in quantity, there is sufficient water power to manufacture steel by the electric furnace methods. Their one great resource is hydroelectric power, which is available in both islands, and there are indications that new enterprises in the light industrial field will soon develop. Still, there is something lacking in order to promote real advancement in either old or new industry—the need for skilled research technicians. The economists have urged the creation of a graduate university for industrial research, and, with such action, New Zealand should make great strides in the industrial world.

Farming, on the other hand, already offers great opportunities to the people of New Zealand. The meat industry is especially encouraging, as great quantities of meat are exported annually; and, strange as it may seem, butter and cheese are also high on the list of exports. The largest industrial plants are freezing plants, and New Zealand is the world's largest exporter of mutton and lamb. As you probably know, the New Zealanders are great lamb and mutton eaters, and, quite fortunately for us visiting servicemen, we had all of the steaks we wanted to eat while we were there. Although frozen lamb and mutton can be kept in good condition almost indefinitely, beef is spoiled somewhat by freezing and, when chilled, will keep fresh for a limited time only. Thus, for many years New Zealand beef competed poorly with that from countries nearer the main markets for such products. In 1933 it was discovered that chilled beef would keep longer with carbon dioxide in the storage hold of the ships, and, when carried by the fastest ships on the Panama route, such beef compares favorably with the Argentine product. The agricultural prospects, then, are good, but what about the development in mineral production?

Compared with really great producers of minerals, there is not a large quantity of minerals being mined in New Zealand. The first comers to the country were not goldseekers, as was the case in Australia. Even though there have been two minor gold booms in the country, such an industry has never been very important. At the present time, about 600,000 ounces of gold are being produced annually, which brings in about $4,500,000. In regard to coal production, they cannot compare in coal mining even to our one state of Pennsylvania since their supplies of coal are so limited that only about 2,500,000 tons of coal are mined annually. The largest coal sources are bituminous, brown coal is second in production, and lignite is third. Some of the factors which make coal mining expensive are the thinness, folding, and faulting of veins, and the depth at which coal is found because most of the coal mines are located 2,500 feet or more below sea level. They do have one mineral which we don't produce at all. That mineral is kauri gum, which is really the fossilized resin of kauri trees destroyed long ago. It is a clear, amber-like substance, and it is made into ornaments, as well as used as a base for varnish or lacquers. Now, in addition to the minerals already mentioned, there is small-scale mining for mercury, manganese ore, tungsten, sulphur, asbestos, tin, platinum, and phosphates, but, even so, I want to make it clear that New Zealand is definitely not a mining country.

I think it is surprising to know that even though the total volume of commodity trade is not large in comparison with that of other countries, it is the highest in the world on a per capita scale. New Zealand has developed principally as a source of primary products or raw materials. That certainly explains why most of her exports are of this nature. Where do her exports go? Eighty percent of her exports are made to the United Kingdom, and the United States receives only about 5 percent of her exports. She ranks third among wool-exporting countries, and about 85 percent of her sheepskins go to the United States. Her imports, on the other hand, are articles that have been wholly or mainly manufactured. From the United Kingdom she receives about half of her imports, and our own country contributes about 12 percent of her imports. As you would expect, motor cars, agricultural implements and machinery, and electrical machinery and apparatus rank high in the imports she receives. Some of the minor items which New Zealand imports include chemicals and drugs, sugar, tobacco, and alcoholic liquors. In order to control her imports, a system of import control was in effect for many years, but since the war the control has been repealed. The reason for this is that the normal course of trade was seriously disturbed during the war years, and after the war the people were interested in further enlarging the import quotas rather than in cutting them. Two contributing forces to import demands came from the New Zealand soldier of World War II, who saw what goods were available from other parts of the world, and the contact of the civilian population of New Zealand with the American troops, which also served to promote a demand for the products which the American possessed or talked about.

This evening I wish to emphasize that the modern Pacific area is evolving rapidly. This area has emerged as one where the most vital, social, economic, and political issues of this century are being decided for good or for ill. During the last war New Zealand was an outpost from which our troops were able to begin their trip up to Japan, and it was a convenient place for the stockpiling of American goods ready for the push-off attack against a common enemy. We recognized then the value of New Zealand and the Pacific islands, and, as a result, there was opened for us a new geography.

In New Zealand we found a progressive-minded people. In a little more than a century they have transformed themselves from primitive wilderness into one of the most productive and progressing democracies in the world. The American soldiers asked New Zealanders many questions about their political and economic policies. In talking with them, we found them a people who received some of their ideas of government from the American colonist, and who have parallels with the history of America in such a way that they can declare a faith in the democratic way of life. But most important, they are a people who like American ideas, and they like the American system of "know how." New Zealand seems to be a nation with a bright future.

Listening Test

On the basis of the speech you have just heard, please answer the following questions. They are all of the multiple-choice type. Choose the answer you consider the *best,* and circle the number.

1.   Of the two men in the conversation described in the talk, the occupation of the man from New Zealand is: (1) farming; (2) dairying; (3) manufacturing; (4) not stated.

2.   The highest mountains of the country are: (1) all volcanic in nature, (2) partly volcanic in nature; (3) not volcanic in nature; (d) not defined in nature.

3.   The lakes are not used for transportation purposes because: (1) they are short; (2) they are at high altitudes; (3) they are shallow; (4) they are poorly situated.

4.   The main use of the rivers is for: (1) water transportation; (2) scenic beauty; (3) waterpower; (4) commercial fishing.

5.   There are two main harbors and their location is: (1) in North Island; (2) in South Island; (3) one in North Island and the other in South Island; (4) not specified.

6.   The range in temperatures is very slight and: (1) the north is the coolest; (2) the middle belt is the coolest; (3) the south is the coolest; (4) the extreme north and south are the coolest.

7.   Rainfall for the whole country is: (1) lacking; (2) adequate; (3) average; (4) plentiful.

8.   New Zealand was discovered and settled in: (1) 1000 A.D.; (2) 400 A.D.; (3) 700 A.D.; (4) 900 A.D.

9.   The natives of the Pacific made their exploration with the help of: (1) movements of the stars; (2) crude instruments and mathematics; (3) movements of the stars and birds; (4) mathematics and common sense.

10.   Captain James Cook took possession of New Zealand after landing on: (1) South Island; (2) islands of the coast; (3) North Island; (4) the mainlands.

11.   The reason for not colonizing the country by England was due to: (1) their bad experiences with the American Colonies; (2) the great distance separating the two countries; (3) the lack of people interested in colonizing; (4) the lack of money for colonization.

12.   A settlement was started in North Auckland because: (1) it was on a trade route; (2) the natives wanted liquor and muskets; (3) food, flax, and lumber were plentiful; (4) a missionary wanted to convert the natives.

13.   The end of the conflict between the natives and colonists came in: (1) 1840; (2) 1857; (3) 1867; (4) 1877.

14.   New Zealand is subject to Great Britain in regard to: (1) taxes; (2) war; (3) tariffs; (4) none of these.

149

15. The upper house of government has the power to: (1) initiate taxation; (2) initiate spending bills; (3) initiate general legislation; (4) amend taxation.

16. Elections to the lower house are held every: (1) 2 years; (2) 4 years; (3) 5 years; (4) 3 years.

17. The members of the executive branch of the government are: (1) elected by the people; (2) chosen by the lower house; (3) elected by the majority party; (4) chosen by the majority party.

18. The political party recently defeated at the polls was: (1) the National party; (2) the Labor party; (3) the Socialist party; (4) the People's party.

19. The proportion of people engaged in farming has: (1) steadily increased; (2) remained the same; (3) steadily decreased; (4) gradually increased.

20. The advancement of manufacturing industries has been slow because of: (1) the lack of steel; (2) the lack of coal; (3) the lack of iron ore; (4) all of these.

21. The largest industrial plants are: (1) the electric plants; (2) the freezing plants; (3) the dairy plants; (4) the manufacturing plants.

22. Gold production is limited, but each year the total reaches about: (1) $1½ million; (2) $2½ million; (3) $4½ million; (4) $6½ million.

23. The largest resources in coal are: (1) brown coal; (2) soft coal; (3) lignite; (4) bituminous.

24. Kauri gum is a mineral that is derived from: (1) sap from kauri trees; (2) fossilized resin from kauri trees; (3) pulp from kauri trees; (4) leaves of kauri trees.

25. On a per capita basis of commodity trade New Zealand ranks: (1) low; (2) average; (3) highest; (4) high.

26. The major exports of New Zealand are: (1) mineral products; (2) fish products; (3) wood products; (4) all of these.

27. Among wool-exporting countries New Zealand ranks: (1) first; (2) second; (3) third; (4) fourth.

28. The major imports she receives include: (1) electric machinery; (2) motor cars; (3) agricultural implements; (4) all of these.

29. Of her minor imports she receives all but one of the following: (1) liquors; (2) fertilizers; (3) sugar; (4) chemicals.

30. A system of import control is: (1) still in effect; (2) temporarily laid aside; (3) no longer required; (4) required to solve problems.

31. The role of New Zealand in the last war was: (1) as an outpost for troops; (2) a place for a stockpile of goods; (3) both of these; (4) none of these.

32. The jump from a primitive wilderness to a progressive democracy has been accomplished in: (1) one century; (2) a little more than a century; (3) a little less than a century; (4) much less than a century.

33. For an accurate description of New Zealand, all but one of the following statements is helpful: (1) they have no king; (2) they are under British domination; (3) they are not a part of Australia; (4) they keep their own taxes.

Chapter 6
Social Groups

The dissemination of information is necessary in many small group situations. For example, the successful completion of a group task may depend in large part on the availability of information to each individual involved in the task. Maintaining social relations among friends is often dependent upon transmitting information from one to another. Such information is available only to the extent that members of a group have ways of communicating with one another. Individuals who communicate with only certain of, say, a community, dormitory, department, family, or church are limited to the information available to those members and are excluded from the information that the other members have. Whenever we communicate with others, however restrictive or open we may be, face-to-face, word-of-mouth contact is at the core of information diffusion.

The experiments that follow attempt to demonstrate how we participate in information diffusion. Do you have acquaintances to whom you will transmit information about these experiments and this course? You may be in a national network of communication such as those studied by Milgram. Let the folks know.

Study 6.1
Acquaintance Networks

Proposition
Acquaintance networks facilitate the widespread diffusion of information.

Research Questions
Given two unacquainted people, how many intermediate acquaintances does it take to connect them?

What kinds of acquaintance networks exist in a social system?

To what extent do acquaintance networks cross ethnic groups, social classes, and occupational groups?

Research Methods*

Subjects

Thirty volunteers who are all residents of the same part of a geographical area consisting of approximately 100,000 or more residents. The area may be a city or county within a state. These subjects will be the *starting population*.

One *target person* who lives in the most remote location within the geographical area from the 30 starters. The target person should be unacquainted with the starters.

Materials

A small manila envelope for each starter containing a description of the study ("This Is a Communication Research Project"), the name and other selected information about the target person, Four Steps for Participation in This Study, a roster to which each participant and intermediary is to affix his or her name, and a stack of 15 reply postcards (with stamps) asking for information about each intermediary, one to be mailed to the experimenter by each intermediary.

Procedures

1. Selection and Preparation of Subjects
   a. Contact a target person who lives in a remote part of the city or county and who would most likely be unknown to the starting population. Secure agreement from that person to serve as the target, and get the following information for inclusion in the envelope for starters: name, address, occupation, place of employment, college or high school and year of graduation, military service dates, wife's maiden name and hometown or husband's name and hometown (if the target is married).
   b. Contact 30 starters from another part of the city or county who do not know the target. Explain what the starters are going to do, and secure their agreement to participate. Provide starters with a copy of the manila envelope containing the appropriate materials. Also, include an envelope in which to mail the packet to the second link.
2. Conduct of the Experiment
   a. Each starter is to hand or mail the manila envelope to a personal acquaintance who is more likely than the starter to know the target person. The intermediary can be a friend, relative, or acquaintance, but it must be someone who is known personally by the starter.
   b. The rules for participation included in the envelope contain the same instructions for people whether they are receiving the envelope from a starter or from another intermediary. Each intermediary is instructed to take one of the postcards, fill it out, and mail it back to the experimenter. The intermediary is to add his or her name to the roster included in the envelope in order to prevent people from sending the envelope to someone who has already received it. Then the intermediary will pass the

*Adapted from an experiment reported in Jeffrey Travers and Stanley Milgram, "An Experimental Study of the Small World Problem," *Sociometry,* Vol. 32 (Dec. 1969), pp. 425–432. By permission.

envelope on to a person he or she feels may know the target person. One of the intermediaries may eventually hand or mail the envelope to the target person.

c. The tracer postcards are designed to enable experimenters to keep track of the progress of each chain as it develops. The following information is requested from each intermediary (or sender): name, address, sex, age, occupation, and spouse (if married); the name, address, sex, and age of the recipient; the relationship between the sender and the recipient (friend, relative, business associate); and a brief explanation of the reason that particular individual was chosen as a recipient of the envelope.

d. Allow approximately one month for the envelopes to arrive at the target. Arrange with the target to inform you when an envelope arrives so that you may pick it up and begin the process of charting the number of links and the channels. A study on which this procedure is based had only 30 percent of the chains completed to the target. When 10 envelopes have arrived, you should proceed with a data analysis. The tracer cards will provide information about incomplete chains, which may be used for comparisons.

3. Tabulation of the Data

a. Count the number of *intermediaries* involved in each completed chain. Do *not* count either the starter or the target. Plot the data on a frequency polygon as below.

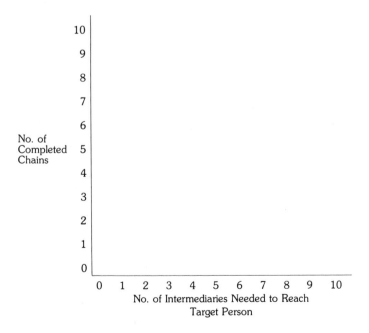

b. Tabulate the number of males who sent the envelope on to males, the males who sent to females, the females who sent to females, and the females who sent to males. Portray the data in a table as below; data are available from tracer cards.

Link	Participant Contact by Sex	
	Frequency	
Female to Female		
Male to Male		
Female to Male		
Male to Female		

c. Tabulate the number of times an envelope was sent to a friend, a relative, or an acquaintance; the data should be available from tracer cards. Portray the data in a table.

Link	Participant Contact by Relationship
	Frequency
Friend	
Acquaintance	
Relative	

d. What are the predominant occupations of the intermediaries?
e. How could intermediaries be categorized according to age?
f. What were the major reasons given for selecting a particular recipient-intermediary?
g. What were some of the characteristics of incomplete chains?

Name _____   Section _____

Date _____   Instructor _____

Results

1. How many of the chains were actually completed?

2. Were chains with predominantly male-to-male links completed more often than others?

3. If you wanted to send a message by means of acquaintance networks, what would be the most likely combination of links to use? (Think in terms of age, sex, occupation, and relationship.)

4. What seemed the most apparent reason for the failure to complete chains?

Explanation

1. Write a concise summary of this experiment and the results obtained.

2. What conclusions can be drawn from this experiment about information diffusion?

This Is a Communication Research Project

We need your help in an unusual study being conducted by (department and university name). We are attempting to find out how certain kinds of communication contacts take place. We are wondering whether it is possible for information to be transmitted to a target person by someone who has never met that person. We wonder how many in-between people are necessary to get the information from one person to another if each person passes it along only to people who are friends or acquaintances.

You will notice that this letter has come to you from a friend. He or she has aided this study by sending this folder to you. He or she hopes that you will aid the study by forwarding this folder to someone else. The name of the person who sent you this folder is listed on the roster enclosed.

In the box below, you will find the name and address of an American citizen who has agreed to serve as the *target person* in this study. The idea of the study is to transmit this envelope to the target person by using only a chain of your friends and acquaintances.

Target Person

(Name, address, and information
about the target person
is placed here.)

How to take part in this study is described on the next page.

Four Steps for Participation in This Study

1.   Add your name to the roster below so that the next person who receives this letter will know who sent it.

2.   Fill out one of the postcards, and mail it. No stamp is needed. The postcard is very important because it allows us to keep track of the progress of the envelope as it moves toward the target person.

3.   If you know the target person on a personal basis, mail this folder directly to him or her. Do this only if you have previously met the target person and know each other on a first-name basis.

4.   If you do not know the target person on a personal basis, do not try to contact him or her directly. Instead, hand carry or mail this envelope (postcards and all) to a personal acquaintance who is more likely than you to know the target person. You may send or give the envelope to a friend, relative, or acquaintance, but it must be someone you know on a first-name basis.

Roster		
1		9
2		10
3		11
4		12
5		13
6		14
7		15
8		16

Please sign your name in the next blank space.

Remember, the aim is to move this envelope toward the target person, using only a chain of friends and acquaintances. On first thought, you may feel that you do not know anyone who is acquainted with the target person. This is natural, but at least you can start it moving in the right direction! Who among your acquaintances might conceivably move in the same social circles as the target person? The real challenge is to identify among your friends and acquaintances a person who can advance the folder toward the target person. It may take several steps beyond your friend to get to the target person, but what counts is to start the envelope on its way! The person who receives this folder will then repeat the process until the folder is received by the target person. May we ask you to begin now!

Every person who participates in this study is entitled to a report describing the results of the study.

Please transmit this folder within twenty-four hours. Your help is greatly appreciated.

Sincerely yours,
(Experimenter)

Sample Post Card

Please fill in this information about yourself.

My name:

My address:

My occupation:

My age:

My sex:

Please check here if you would like a copy of a report of the results of this study:

☐

Please fill in this information about the person to whom you are sending the envelope.

His/her name:

His/her address:

His/her occupation:

His/her approximate age:

His/her sex:

Nature of his/her relationship to you (friend, relative, acquaintance, etc.)

Briefly, why did you select this person to receive the envelope?

Please mail this completed post card as soon as possible.

Experiment 6.2
Communication Patterns in Small Groups

Proposition
The communication pattern through which information flows affects the efficiency of a small group.

Research Questions
What effect does a fixed communication pattern have upon a group's ability to solve problems?

What is the effect of different fixed communication patterns on the amount of time it takes to solve a problem, on the number of interactions required to solve a problem, and on the satisfaction members express at the end of a problem-solving period?

Research Methods*

Subjects
Three, 6, or 9 groups of 5 individuals each.

One timekeeper for each group.

Two observers for each group.

Materials
Three, 6, or 9 sets of 8½″ × 11″ cards with letters A, B, C, D, and E printed on them for marking chairs.

Copies of the NASA Ranking Task for each member of each group.

Copies of the Group Member Satisfaction Scale for each member of each group.

Copies of Observer Recording Form for each observer.

Procedures
1. Preparation of Subjects
   a. Arrange 3 sets of chairs in the patterns indicated below, and mark each chair with the letter indicated. Separate the sets as soon as possible.

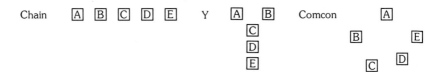

*Adapted from an experiment reported in Bonnie Lackey and Jerry Rubier, "The Effects of Communication Network on Attitude Change," manuscript prepared for Speech Communication 514, Seminar in Small Group Communication, University of Montana, Summer 1971. By permission.

2. Conduct of the Experiment
   a. Seat the subjects, and explain the procedures of the experiment.

   This is a study of the way in which fixed communication patterns influence how groups complete tasks. Thus, you will be given a task to accomplish as a group. At the same time, you will be restricted in the ways in which you can communicate. That is, you will be limited in terms of who you can talk to, as follows:

   Y: A may talk only to C.
         B may talk only to C.
         C may talk to A, B, or D.
         D may talk to C and E.
         E may talk only to D.

   Chain: A may talk only to B.
           B may talk to A and C.
           C may talk to B and D.
           D may talk to C and E.
           E may talk only to D.

   Comcon: Talk to anyone you wish in any order you like.

   b. Ask the timekeeper to join each group and to record the time from the time the group begins communicating until it finishes the task. The timekeeper should also watch for violations in who talks to whom and gently make corrections to conform with the assignments.
   c. Ask the group observers to take seats near their group but to avoid disturbing the group interaction as they observe and chart who talks to whom.
   d. Distribute copies of the NASA Ranking Task to each member of each group, with directions to begin as soon as each member has read the task instructions and understood the task.
   e. As each group completes the task, or at the end of 20 to 30 minutes, stop the groups, and ask them to arrive at a ranking; distribute the Group Member Satisfaction Scales to each participant. They should complete the scales immediately and hand them to the timekeeper.
   f. Distribute copies of the NASA Exercise Answer Sheet (to be provided by your instructor), and have the timekeeper score the differences between the group rankings and the key.
3. Tabulation of the Data
   a. Record the number of points difference between the key and the group rankings.

	Points Difference
Chain	
Y	
Comcon	

b. Record the number of minutes each group took to complete the task.

	Time
Chain	
Y	
Comcon	

c. Tally the number of messages sent by each member in each group.

	Total No. of Messages				
	A	B	C	D	E
Chain					
Y					
Comcon					

d. Tally the scores on each scale of the Group Member Satisfaction Scale Form.

	Like Position				
	A	B	C	D	E
Chain					
Y					
Comcon					

	Group Work				
	A	B	C	D	E
Chain					
Y					
Comcon					

	Agree with Ranking				
	A	B	C	D	E
Chain					
Y					
Comcon					

Results

1.   Which pattern of communication seemed to be the most efficient—that is, which pattern completed the task in the least amount of time with the fewest number of interactions?

2.   Which group seemed to be the most satisfied with their work—that is, they liked what they did both as individuals and as a group?

3.   Does there seem to be a relationship between individual satisfaction and the extent to which subjects agreed with the group ranking?

Explanation

1.   Write a concise summary of this experiment and the results obtained.

2.   Given the opportunity to use a fixed communication pattern to solve a problem, which network would you select, and why?

NASA Ranking Task

Instructions: You are a member of a space crew originally scheduled to rendezvous with a mother ship on the lighted surface of the moon. Because of mechanical difficulties, however, your ship was forced to land at a spot some 200 miles from the rendezvous point. During landing, much of the equipment aboard was damaged, and since survival depends on reaching the mother ship, the most critical items available must be chosen for the 200-mile trek. Below are listed the 15 items left intact and undamaged after landing. Your task is to rank order them in terms of their importance to your crew in allowing them to reach the rendezvous point. Place the number 1 by the most important item, number 2 by the second most important item, and so on, through number 15, the least important.

This is a group decision-making task. Your group is to employ the method of *group consensus* in reaching its decision on the rankings. Since consensus is difficult to reach, try as a group to make each ranking one with which *all* group members can at least partially agree.

____ Box of matches
____ Food concentrate
____ 50 feet of nylon rope
____ Parachute silk
____ Portable heating unit
____ Two .45 calibre pistols
____ One case of dehydrated Pet milk
____ Two 100-lb. tanks of oxygen
____ Stellar map of moon's constellation
____ Life raft
____ Magnetic compass
____ 5 gallons of water
____ Signal flares
____ First aid kit containing injection needles
____ Solar-powered FM receiver-transmitter

Group Member Satisfaction Scale

Place a checkmark along each scale that most nearly represents your feelings.

1. How much did you like your position in the group?

Strongly
Disliked ___ : ___ : ___ : ___ : ___ : ___ : ___ Strongly
          1   2   3   4   5   6   7 Liked

2. How well did your group work together?

Very Poorly ___ : ___ : ___ : ___ : ___ : ___ : ___ Very Well
          1   2   3   4   5   6   7

3. To what extent did you agree with the final ranking of the group?

Not at All ___ : ___ : ___ : ___ : ___ : ___ : ___ Completely
         1   2   3   4   5   6   7

Model for Cards to Use in Marking Chairs

(Use 8½ × 11-inch paper or cards.)

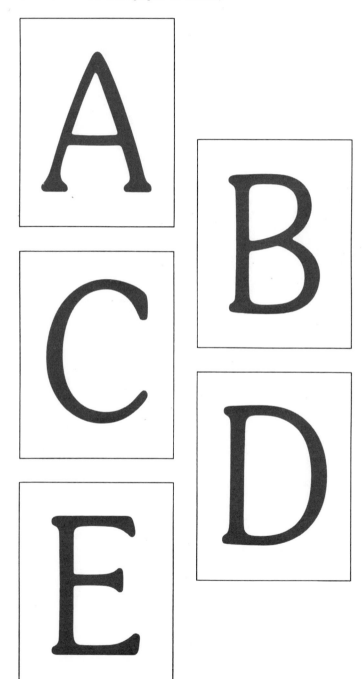

Chapter 7
Serial Groups

When a two-person dyad is expanded so that a message is relayed through a series of interactions in which each person's reproduction of a message becomes the message which the next person receives, the system by which information is diffused is called *serial communication*. This process is sometimes called *social memory* since information is retained and reproduced through a series of individual memories and reports. Serial communication experiments are usually conducted to determine what kind and how many changes occur when information is spread by word of mouth.

Experiment 7.1
Serial Reproduction of Information

Proposition
In the serial reproduction of information, details of a message become leveled (omitted), sharpened (highlighted), assimilated (modified to interests), and added.

Research Questions
Does the reproduction of a message in serial form result in changes in the message?

How does familiarity with the story theme influence reproductions?

How does the conceptual completeness of the story that is reproduced influence reproductions?

Research Methods*

Subjects

Ten subjects equated for rote memory ability and (preferable but not essential) majoring in some aspect of business or secretarial science.

Materials

Rote Memory Test.

Original version of the "War of the Ghosts" story recorded on tape.

Explicated version of the "War of the Ghosts" story recorded on tape.

The "Sneak Attacks" story recorded on tape.

Copies of all three stories marked by divisions into constituent themes and information units.

Instructions for Scoring Reproductions.

Tape recorder (cassette or reel-to-reel).

Typewriter and paper for transcribing recorded reproductions.

Procedures

1. Selection of Subjects
   a. Identify a class containing subjects majoring in some aspect of business or secretarial science. Secure permission to select subjects.
   b. Administer the Rote Memory Test to the entire class. Read the passage to to class twice, and instruct them to reproduce as much of it as they can verbatim. Tally the number of words reproduced exactly. Select the 10 superior subjects for the experiment.
   c. Ask subjects to appear at the experimental area at an appointed time.
2. Conduct of the Experiment
   a. As subjects arrive, divide them into 2 chains of 5 individuals each, and assign each member of the chain a letter (A, B, C, D, E).
   b. Using the "reproduction matrix" below, assign a sequence for the appearance of each subject in the actual experimental area.

```
A  B  C  D  E  F  G  H
B  D  H  F  C  A  E  G
C  H  E  B  G  D  A  F
D  F  B  H  A  G  C  E
E  C  G  A  H  B  F  D
F  A  D  G  B  E  H  C
G  E  A  C  F  H  D  B
H  G  F  E  D  C  B  A
```

*Adapted from experiments reported in I. H. Paul, "Studies in Remembering," *Psychological Issues*, Vol. 1 (Monograph 2, 1959), pp. 10–60, and E. E. Levitt, "A Quantitative Investigation of Individual Differences in Serial Reproduction: A Contribution to the Study of Rumor," Doctoral dissertation, Columbia University, 1952. By permission of International Universities Press, Inc.

c. Invite the first subject to a table where a microphone is located leading to the tape recorder. Request all other subjects to remain in an area where they can neither hear nor see the subject participating in the reproduction.

d. Explain to the subject that his or her task will be to listen attentively to the tape-recorded story and then to repeat to the next subject what he or she heard as accurately as possible. Explain that the story will be played twice.

e. Play the original version of the "War of the Ghosts" story twice to Subject 1.

f. Turn off the recorder, and explain that the subject may take as long as he or she would like to review the story. Ask Subject 1 to signal as soon as he or she is ready to repeat the story to Subject 2.

g. Upon a signal from Subject 1, ask Subject 2 to enter the room and take a seat across from Subject 1.

h. Explain to Subject 2 that he or she is to listen attentively to Subject 1 tell a story. Instruct Subject 1 to take as much time as is necessary to tell the story as accurately as possible. Subject 2 may ask questions of clarification but may *not* repeat part or all of the story to Subject 1. Turn on the tape recorder, and ask Subject 1 to begin.

i. As soon as Subject 1 has told the story to his or her satisfaction, turn off the tape recorder, and ask Subject 1 to wait in another room until all 5 subjects have finished.

j. Call in Subject 3, and have Subject 2 tell the story to him or her. Use the same instructions for each subject. Record the reproduction of each subject for later transcription and analysis. Subject 3 tells the story to Subject 4, Subject 4 tells it to Subject 5, and Subject 5 tells it to Subject 1.

k. As soon as the first chain of 5 subjects has reproduced the original version of the ghost story, bring in Subject 1 of the second chain and play the explicated version of the "War of the Ghosts" story.

l. Have the second chain of subjects reproduce the explicated version in the same manner as the first group.

m. As soon as the second chain of 5 subjects has reproduced the explicated version of the "War of the Ghosts" story, ask the subjects from the first chain to return; then play the "Sneak Attacks" story for the first subject. Use a different sequence taken from the reproduction matrix.

n. Have the first chain reproduce the "Sneak Attacks" story as before.

o. Have the second chain reproduce the "Sneak Attacks" story also. Use a different sequence from the reproduction matrix.

p. You should end up with 20 reproductions on tape—5 reproductions of the original version of the "War of the Ghosts" story, 5 reproductions of the explicated version of the "War of the Ghosts" story, and 10 reproductions of the "Sneak Attacks" story.

q. Have typewritten transcriptions made of the 20 reproductions, being careful to identify each reproduction according to its original stimulus story and its position in the reproduction chain.

3. Tabulation of the Data
   a. Count all of the words in each one of the typed transcripts of the repro-
      ductions.

	No. of Words	
	Original Group	Explicated Group
"War of the Ghosts" Story Repro. No. 1		
Repro. No. 2		
Repro. No. 3		
Repro. No. 4		
Repro. No. 5		
"Sneak Attacks" Story Repro. No. 1		
Repro. No. 2		
Repro. No. 3		
Repro. No. 4		
Repro. No. 5		

   b. Tally the number of "information units" in each reproduction, using the
      marked copies of the original stimulus materials. Sum the scores for
      each reproduction.

	No. of Info. Units	
	Original Group	Explicated Group
"War of the Ghosts" Story Repro. No. 1		
Repro. No. 2		
Repro. No. 3		
Repro. No. 4		
Repro. No. 5		
"Sneak Attacks" Story Repro. No. 1		
Repro. No. 2		
Repro. No. 3		
Repro. No. 4		
Repro. No. 5		

c. Tally the presence of themes in each of the reproductions of each of the chains, and arrive at a "theme score" for each reproduction.

	No. of Themes	
	Original Group	Explicated Group
"War of the Ghosts" Story Repro. No. 1		
Repro. No. 2		
Repro. No. 3		
Repro. No. 4		
Repro. No. 5		
"Sneak Attacks" Story Repro. No. 1		
Repro. No. 2		
Repro. No. 3		
Repro. No. 4		
Repro. No. 5		

Name _____   Section _____

Date _____   Instructor _____

Results

1. Which story was reproduced most accurately? That is, which story had the highest number of words, units, and themes at the fifth reproduction?

2. At which reproduction did the greatest loss in information units occur?

3. What do the data reveal about the loss, addition, highlighting, and assimilation of details during reproduction? Did any of the above occur?

4. What kinds of distortions occurred during reproductions?

5. Did any subjects tend to elaborate or expand upon the preceding story (their stimulus story)?

6. To what extent would you agree with the following conclusion: "It is now perfectly clear that serial reproduction normally brings about startling and radical alterations in the material dealt with."

Explanation

1. Write a concise summary of this experiment and the results obtained.

2. Would you agree that our memory is exceedingly subject to error and that serial reproduction accentuates errors by having a series of initial reproductions in which the loss of information is the greatest?

3. Were the research questions answered by the data?

Rote Memory Test

The Thunder Dreamer knows that in the sky dwell the warriors of Thunder and Lightning. He has seen and spoken to them in his vision. These braves ride wildly about in the black clouds on their handsome horses, holding in their hands the fire sticks which flash during a storm.

Original Version: The War of the Ghosts

One night two young men from Egulac went down to the river to hunt seals, and while they were there it became foggy and calm. They stopped their work and hearkened. Then they heard war cries, and they thought, "Maybe this is a war party." They escaped to the shore and hid behind a log. Now canoes came up, and they heard the noise of paddles and saw one canoe coming up to them. There were five men in the canoe, and they said,

"What do you think? We wish to take you along. We are going up the river to make war on the people."

"I will not go along," one of the young men said. "I might be killed. My relatives do not know where I have gone. But you," he said, turning to the other, "may go with them."

So one of the young men went, but the other returned home.

And the warriors went up on the river to a town on the other side of Kalama. The people came down to the water, and they began to fight, and many were killed. But presently the young man heard one of the warriors say, "Quick, let us go home; that Indian has been hit." Now he thought, "Oh, they are ghosts." He did not feel sick, but they said he had been shot.

So the canoes went back to Egulac, and the young man went ashore to his house and made a fire. He rested, then he ate, and he thought, "I must tell everybody my adventure." So he told everybody and said, "Behold I accompanied the ghosts, and we went to fight. Many of our fellows were killed, and many of those who attacked us were killed. They said I was hit, and I did not feel sick."

He told it all, and then he became quiet. When the sun rose, he fell down. Something black came out of his mouth. His face became contorted. The people jumped up and cried.

He was dead.

Original Version Marked: The War of the Ghosts

(a)One night/two/young/men/from Egulac/went down/to the river/to hunt/seals,/
(b)and while they were there/it became foggy/and calm./ (c)They stopped/their
work/and hearkened./ (d)Then they heard/war cries,/and they thought,/"Maybe
this is a war party."/ (e)They escaped/to the shore,/and hid/behind a log./ (f)Now
canoes/came up,/and they heard/the noise of paddles/and saw/one canoe/coming
up to them./ (g)There were five/men/in the canoe,/and they said,/

"What do you think?/We wish to take you along./ (h)We are going/up the river/
to make war/on the people."/

(i)"I will not go along,"/one/of the young men/said./"I might be killed./My rela-
tives/do not know/where I have gone./ (j)But you,"/he said,/turning to the other,/
"may go with them."/

(k)So one/of the young men/went,/but the other/returned home./

(l)And the warriors/went on up/the river/to a town/on the other side/of Kalama./
(m)The people/came down to the water,/and they began/to fight,/and many were
killed./ (n)But presently/the young man/heard/one/of the warriors/say,/"Quick,
let us go home;/that Indian/has been hit."/ (p)Now he thought,/"Oh, they are
ghosts."/ (q)He did not feel sick,/but they said/he had been shot./

(s)So the canoes/went back/to Egulac,/and the young man/went ashore/to his
house/and made a fire./ (t)He rested,/then he ate,/and he thought,/"I must tell/
everybody/my adventure."/ (u)So he told/everybody/and said:/"Behold I accom-
panied/the ghosts,/and we went to fight./Many/of our fellows/were killed,/and
many/of those who attacked us/were killed./ (v)They said/I was hit,/and I did not
feel sick."/

(w)He told it all,/and then he became quiet./When the sun/rose,/he fell down./
Something/black/came out/of his mouth./His face/became contorted./ (x)The peo-
ple/jumped up/and cried./

(y)He was dead./

This version is divided into constituent themes and information units. The themes are marked by
letters (a, b, c, etc.), and the information units are marked by crossbars (/).

Explicated Version: The War of the Ghosts

One night two young men from Egulac went down to the river to fish, and while they were there, it became foggy and calm. They knew this was an omen of ghosts. Then they heard war cries, and they thought, "Maybe this is a war party."

They escaped to the shore and hid behind a log. But there was no hiding from these canoes. One canoe came straight up to them. There were five men in the canoe, and they said,

"We are going up the river to make war on the people. We wish to take you along. What do you think?"

"I will not go along," one of the young men said. "I might be killed. My relatives do not know where I have gone. But you," he said, turning to the other, "have no relatives, so you may go with them."

So one of the young men went, but the other returned home.

And the warriors went on up the river to a town on the other side of Kalama. The people came down to the water, and they began to fight, and many were killed. But presently the young man heard one of the warriors say, "Quick, let us go home; that Indian has been hit." Now he thought, "My fellows do not call me 'Indian.' Oh, they surely are ghosts." He did not feel sick, but they said he had been shot. Ghosts' company, he remembered, gives protection from pain and death while the night lasts.

So the canoes went back to Egulac, and the young man went ashore to his house and made a fire to summon everybody. And he told them, "Behold I accompanied the ghosts, and we went to fight. Many of our fellows were killed, and many of those who attacked us were killed. They said I was hit, and I did not feel sick."

He told it all, and then he became quiet. When the sun rose, he fell down. Something black came out of his mouth. His face became contorted. The people jumped up and cried.

He was dead.

Explicated Version Marked: The War of the Ghosts

(a) One night/two/young/men/from Egulac/went down/to the river/to fish,/and/ *(b)* while they were there,/it became foggy/and calm./ *(c)* They knew/this/was an omen/of ghosts./ *(d)* Then they heard/war cries,/and they thought,/"Maybe this is a war party."/ *(e)* They escaped/to the shore/and hid/behind a log./ *(f)* But there was/no hiding/from these canoes./One canoe/came straight/up to them./ *(g)* There were five/men/in the canoe,/and they said,/

(h) "We are going/up the river/to make war/on the people./ *(i)* We wish/to take you along./What do you think?"/

(j) "I will not go along,"/one/of the young men/said./"I might be killed./My relatives/do not know/where I have gone./ *(k)* But you,"/he said,/turning to the other,/ "have no relatives,/so you may go with them."/

(l) So one/of the young men/went,/but the other/returned home./

(m) And the warriors/went on up/the river/to a town/on the other side/of Ka-lama./ *(n)* The people/came down to the water,/and they began/to fight,/and many/ were killed./ *(o)* But presently/the young man/heard/one/of the warriors/say,/ "Quick, let us go home;/that Indian/has been hit."/ *(p)* Now he thought,/"My fel-lows/do not call/me 'Indian.'/ *(q)* Oh, they surely are ghosts."/ *(r)* He did not feel sick,/but they said/he had been shot./ *(s)* Ghosts' company,/he remembered,/gives protection/from pain/and death/while the night lasts./

(t) So the canoes/went back/to Egulac,/and the young man/went ashore/to his house/and made a fire/to summon/everybody./ *(u)* And he told them,/"Behold I accompanied/the ghosts,/and we went to fight./ *(v)* They said/I was hit,/and I did not feel sick."/

(w) He told it all,/and then he became quiet./When the sun/rose,/he fell down./ Something/black/came out/of his mouth./His face/became contorted./ *(x)* The people/jumped up/and cried./

(y) He was dead./

184

The Sneak Attacks

Two sisters, who graduated from business college in Menasser, decided to go overseas and work in foreign embassies. They said to Mother, "This way we can work
and see the world at the same time." They separated and took jobs in neighboring countries. "Promise you'll write to me every day," they said to each other.
They agreed and parted.

One sister went to Montania, which she found in a state of war hysteria. Her
stenographic competence landed her a position as private secretary to the foreign
minister.

"You will have access to top secret information," he admonished her. "I count
on loyalty."

One day she came across a confidential document. It described a sneak attack
by the Montania air force in which they were going to bomb all of the government
buildings of a small nearby nation. She read the document with interest until she
noted the name of the nation. To her horror she realized that it was where her
sister was working. "Oh, I must write and warn her," she thought. But of course
censorship was invoked between the two countries. She thought desperately how
to save her poor sister. And then she hit on a plan. She would stop writing altogether, and her sister would wonder, then become worried, and probably soon
decide to come and see her to make sure she wasn't ill and needed her help.

On the day she put her plan into action, she did not receive her sister's daily
letter. She wondered. The next day she also got no letter, and she became worried. "It is very unusual that she shouldn't write me," she thought. "Perhaps my
sister is ill."

So she decided straightway to go and see her sister.

The distance was only twelve kilometers, and she figured it would be safest to
walk. At the border she met, of all people, her sister who was coming to visit her,
she soon learned, for the very same reasons.

That day, both nations bombed each other, and the embassies were destroyed.

The Sneak Attacks (Marked)

*(a)*Two/sisters,/who graduated/from business college/in Menasser,/decided to go/overseas/and work/in foreign/embassies./ *(b)*They said/to Mother,/"This way/ we can work/and see the world/at the same time."/ *(c)*They separated/and took jobs/in neighboring countries./ *(d)*"Promise you'll write to me/every day,"/they said/to each other./They agreed/ *(e)*and parted./

One sister went to Montania,/ *(f)*which she found/in a state/of war hysteria./ *(g)*Her stenographic/competence/landed her/a position/as private secretary/to the foreign/minister.

(h)"You/will have access/to top secret/information,"/he admonished her./ "I count on/loyalty."/

*(i)*One day/she came across/a confidential/document./ *(j)*It described/a sneak/ attack/by the Montania/air force/in which they were going to bomb/all/of the govern- ment buildings/of a small/nearby/nation./ *(k)*She read/the document/with interest/ until she noted/the name/of the nation./ *(l)*To her horror/she realized/that it was where/her sister/was working./ *(m)*"Oh, I must write/and warn her,"/she thought./ But of course/censorship/was invoked/between the two countries./*(n)*She thought/ desperately/how to save/her poor sister./ *(o)*And then/she hit on a plan./She would stop/writing altogether,/ *(p)*and her sister/would wonder,/then become wor- ried,/and probably soon/decide/to come and see her/to make sure/she wasn't ill/and needed her help.

*(q)*On the day/she put her plan/into action,/she did not receive/her sister's daily letter. *(r)*She wondered./The next day/she also got no letter,/and she became wor- ried./ *(s)*"It is very unusual/that she shouldn't write me,"/she thought./"Perhaps/ my sister is ill."/

*(t)*So she decided/straightway/to go and see/her sister./

*(u)*The distance/was only/twelve/kilometers,/and she figured/it would be safest/ to walk./ *(v)*At the border/she met,/of all people,/her sister/ *(w)*who was coming to visit her,/she soon learned,/for the very same/reasons./

*(x)*That day,/both nations/bombed/each other,/and the embassies/were destroyed./

Instructions for Scoring Reproductions

1. *Word Count:* Using the typed transcripts of each reproduction for each story, count all words, including "a" and "the."

2. *Information Units:* Score 1 point for each word or series of words in the reproductions that correspond to an information unit in the original stories, even if slightly altered (in tense or by substitution of synonyms). Score 0.5 points for each information unit that is significantly altered yet preserves the sense of the original. Score 0 points for errors, distortions, and units of information with no correspondence to the original stories. Sum the scores for each reproduction, and determine the amount of information accurately reproduced.

3. *Themes:* Score 1 point for the presence of each theme (*a* through *x* or *y*), regardless of the accuracy of detail or sense, by responding to the following list of questions.

 "War of the Ghosts" Story

 Theme a: Does the reproduction tell of a hunting or fishing expedition by the men?

 Theme b: Is some mention made of the atmospheric conditions?

! *Theme c:* Is it mentioned that they stop and/or listen?

* *Theme c:* Is there some portent given of something pending?

 Theme d: Does the reproduction mention that they heard something approaching (war cries or sounds of canoes)?

 Theme e: Do the men hide in some way?

 Theme f: Is there some description of the canoes approaching the men?

 Theme g: Is there mention of an invitation?

 Theme h: Are the plans of the men in the boat mentioned?

 Theme i: Is one man's refusal mentioned?

 Theme j: Does he in some way allow or encourage the other to go?

 Theme k: Is it mentioned that one goes and one doesn't go?

 Theme l: Is the traveling in the canoes mentioned?

 Theme m: Is the battle mentioned or described?

 Theme n: Is it described that someone cries for the battle to cease; or does someone cry out to bring attention to the casualty?

* *Theme o:* Is it mentioned that he is never called "Indian" by his people or that there is something noteworthy about it?

 Theme p: Is it mentioned that the man realizes that he is in the company of ghosts?

 Theme q: Is it mentioned that he is wounded yet feels no pain?

* *Theme r:* Is his knowledge of ghosts' protection mentioned?

 Theme s: Is the return home or to his people mentioned?

! *Theme t:* Is there some mention of his decision to tell his adventure?

 Theme u: Is it described how he tells everyone about his adventure?

 Theme v: Is it mentioned again that he was wounded but felt no pain?

Themes that are unique to the explicated version of the "War of the Ghosts" story are marked with an asterisk (*). Those unique to the original version are marked with an exclamation point (!).

187

Theme w: Is there a description of the morning events? (Any one of the strange afflictions is satisfactory.)

Theme x: Is the reaction of sorrow and/or horror by the people mentioned?

Theme y: Is the man's death mentioned?

"Sneak Attacks" Story

Theme a: Does the reproduction tell of two girls graduating and going to work overseas?

Theme b: Is some mention made of being able to work and see the world?

Theme c: Is there mention of taking jobs in neighboring countries?

Theme d: Is there mention of a promise to write every day?

Theme e: Is there mention of the girls parting, with one going to Montania?

Theme f: Is mention made of war hysteria?

Theme g: Is some mention made of getting a job as a private secretary?

Theme h: Are top secret information and loyalty mentioned?

Theme i: Is there mention of a confidential document?

Theme j: Is there mention of a sneak bomb attack on a nearby nation?

Theme k: Is mention made of reading the document?

Theme l: Is mention made of the sister's horror at realizing it was where her sister worked?

Theme m: Are wanting to write and warn her and censorship mentioned?

Theme n: Is there mention of thinking desperately?

Theme o: Is mention made of the plan to stop writing?

Theme p: Is there mention of her sister's reaction (wonder, worry, and visit)?

Theme q: Is there mention of failing to receive her sister's letter?

Theme r: Is not receiving a letter another day mentioned?

Theme s: Is there mention of one sister wondering whether the other is ill?

Theme t: Is mention made of deciding to leave immediately?

Theme u: Is any mention made of the distance and the decision to walk?

Theme v: Is there mention of the sisters meeting at the border?

Theme w: Is mention made of the reason why the second sister had decided to visit?

Theme x: Is the bombing of both nations and their embassies being destroyed mentioned?

Experiment 7.2
Reducing Error in Serial Communication

Proposition
The use of certain correctives can greatly reduce the number of changes that occur in serial communication.

Research Questions
Does being able to ask questions about a description or explanation immediately following the presentation reduce losses, changes, and additions during a succeeding retelling of the description or explanation? Does giving emphasis to certain key points during a presentation tend to reduce the loss of those points in later oral reproductions of the presentation?

Research Methods*

Subjects
Eighteen students from this class divided into 3 chains of 6 individuals.

Materials
Film, *Hit and Run Driver,* 16 mm, black and white, sound, 10 minutes; available from Albuquerque Police Academy, University of Albuquerque, Albuquerque, New Mexico, or an equivalent film.

Three tape recorders with tapes for recording reproductions.

Three small tables with microphone setups.

Procedures
1. Selection and Preparation of Subjects
    a. Select 18 individuals from the class, and divide them into 3 chains of 6 each. Number the subjects in each chain from 1 to 6.
    b. Ask all Subjects 2 through 6 to leave the room and visit the cafeteria or coffee shop for 30 minutes. An assistant should escort the 15 subjects in order to alert them when they must return to the experimental area.
2. Conduct of the Experiment
    a. Show the class, including the three Subjects 1, the stimulus film, *Hit and Run Driver* (or an equivalent). The film should be introduced by saying:

        You are going to see a film that tells a story. It is your task to understand and to remember the story.

*Adapted from an experiment reported in Curtis Stadstad, "The Factor of Relevance in the Serial Reproduction of Orally Transmitted Information," Master's thesis, University of Montana, 1969. By permission.

b. Immediately after showing the film, bring the three Subjects 1 to the front of the class. Tell them the following:

> You have just seen a film that told a story. As completely and accurately as possible, describe the events depicted in the film to the next person in your chain (Subject 2). Assume you are reporting the methods used to apprehend the guilty person.

c. Place the No. 1 subjects at points in the classroom out of hearing range of one another at small tables with microphone setups leading to the tape recorders.

d. By means of written instructions, inform only Subject 1 of Chain A that he or she is to pay particular attention to *emphasizing* the methods used to apprehend the guilty person as he or she tells the story. The subject should be given the following written instructions:

> As you tell the story, emphasize the methods used in apprehending the guilty person: (1) by making such statements as "this is important to remember," "now pay particular attention to," "here is a key point," and other verbal emphasizers; and (2) by nonverbally signaling significant methods by reducing the rate of your speech when you mention a method of apprehending the guilty person and by pausing just before and gesturing with a finger when you mention a method.

Subjects 1 of Chain B and Chain C will not get any such instructions to emphasize the methods used to apprehend the guilty person.

e. As soon as the story tellers (Subjects 1) have read and understood the written instructions, call in all Subjects 2, and tell them the following:

> You are about to hear an account of an event. Listen as carefully as you can, and try to understand and remember what you hear.

Have Subjects 1 in Chains A and C begin their reports to their respective Subjects 2. Give the following *additional* instructions to Subject 2 in Chain B:

> As soon as the story teller has finished, you may engage in a 2-minute question-and-answer period with the story teller.

Have Subject 1 of Chain B begin his or her report to Subject 2 of Chain B.

f. After Subjects 2 have heard the story from the story tellers and Subject 2 of Chain B has engaged in a two-minute question-and-answer period, dismiss the story tellers (Subjects 1) to join the class in observing. Before all Subjects 3 are called into the room, Subjects 2 should be told the following:

> You have just heard a story. Now you are to tell as completely and accurately as possible the events to the next person in your chain.

Subject 2 in Chain A should then receive the special written instructions, asking him or her to give emphasis to the methods used in apprehending the guilty person.

g. Call in Subjects 3 for all chains.

h.   Give the initial instructions to all Subjects 3; have Chains A and C begin while you give the additional instructions about the question-and-answer period to Subject 3 in Chain B. Then have Subject 3 of Chain B begin.

i.   Follow the above procedure through the completion of the chains. Be certain that all reproductions are taperecorded for later analysis. There should be 18 stories.

j.   If time remains after all the chains have finished, play back to the class the first reproduction (Subject 1) and the last reproduction (Subject 6), and compare the two in terms of length, apparent omissions, additions of details, and changes or distortions of details.

3.   Tabulation of the Data

a.   Have each of the reproductions in all 3 chains transcribed into manuscripts.

b.   Count the number of words in each transcription.

	No. of Words		
	Chain A: Emphasis	Chain B: Questions	Chain C: Control
Repro. 1			
Repro. 2			
Repro. 3			
Repro. 4			
Repro. 5			
Repro. 6			

c.   List and then record the number of methods used to apprehend the guilty person that were included in each reproduction for each chain.

	No. of Methods		
	Chain A: Emphasis	Chain B: Questions	Chain C: Control
Repro. 1			
Repro. 2			
Repro. 3			
Repro. 4			
Repro. 5			
Repro. 6			

d. List and then tally the omissions, additions, and changes made in details during each reproduction as they differ from the details in the film.

	Number								
	Chain A: Emphasis			Chain B: Questions			Chain C: Control		
	Omit.	Add.	Changes	Omit.	Add.	Changes	Omit.	Add.	Changes
Repro. 1									
Repro. 2									
Repro. 3									
Repro. 4									
Repro. 5									
Repro. 6									

e. Interview each of the subjects to identify how they felt about each of the corrective techniques (emphasis or questioning) built into the experiment and how the techniques helped or hindered their reproductions.

Results

1. Which chain ended up with the largest number of details (longest reproductions)?

2. Which chain seemed to retain the largest number of accurate details from reproduction 1 through 6?

3. Where did the largest number of changes occur? Between which two subjects in each chain?

4. According to the reactions of the subjects, which technique seemed to be more effective: emphasizing, asking questions afterwards, or reproducing without either of the techniques?

5. Do these data suggest any advice that ought to be given to police officers about techniques for improving how they get reports of accidents?

6. What other ways of improving the accuracy of information in serial reproductions can you think of?

Explanation

1. Write a concise summary of this experiment and the results obtained.

2. In what ways were the research questions answered by this experiment?

Part 4
Experiments about Achieving Change

Chapter 8
Individual Factors

Persuasive efforts that occur in face-to-face encounters are greatly influenced by such factors as how the person to be persuaded views the communicator or the source of the persuasive messages. That is, our feeling of trust influences the degree to which we are willing to go along with a communicator. Apart from the nature of the message, the personality of the communicator exerts a considerable influence on our willingness to change. Such factors as how attractive the persuader appears to the persuadee, how much the persuadee feels the persuader likes him or her, and how much the persuader indicates that he or she wants to influence the persuadee—all represent aspects of persuasion that relate to individual differences.

These experiments test the effects of some individual factors on bringing about attitude or opinion change. We shall investigate how high credibility affects change and whether or not low credibility sources can also influence others to change their opinions.

Experiment 8.1
Credibility

Proposition
A high credibility source tends to produce more attitude change than a low credibility source.

Research Questions
How does the prestige of a speaker influence the effectiveness of his or her persuasive attempt?

Does a speaker of high prestige influence an audience more than a speaker of low prestige?

Research Methods*

Subjects
Fifty individuals divided into 2 groups; choose either 2 introductory communication classes of 25 each or one class of 50 students.

One speaker with a persuasive voice to record the speech on a tape recorder.

Materials
Two copies of the Opinion Questionnaire for each subject—one copy to be completed before the speech is played and one copy to be completed after the recording is played (100 copies).

One speech that is judged to be potentially persuasive, recorded on a cassette or reel-to-reel audio tape.

One tape recorder to play back the speech.

One Speaker Evaluation Form for each subject (50 copies).

One introduction to establish high credibility.

One introduction to create low credibility.

Procedures
1. Selection of Subjects and Preparation of Materials
   a. Either use this class and divide it into 2 groups of 25 each by randomly assigning subjects to Group 1 and Group 2, or contact 2 instructors of a basic course for permission to conduct the experiment in their classes.
   b. Select a topic (possibly the current college debate proposition), and prepare a persuasive speech of approximately 1,800 words—about 15 minutes when read at 125 words per minute; a slightly expanded first affirmative speech would be satisfactory. As an alternative, use the speech at the end of this experiment.
   c. Have an appropriate speaker record the speech in the most persuasive manner possible. Play the recording to a panel of faculty or advanced students in communication, and determine whether they feel the speech is potentially persuasive. If not, have the speech recorded again.
   d. Write two introductions following the models for this experiment, or use the introductions provided (page 205).
2. Conduct of the Experiment
   a. Approximately one week prior to the experiment, administer to each group of subjects, the Opinion Questionnaire. Calculate the mean opinion score for each group.
   b. Call Group 1 the high prestige or credibility group and Group 2 the low prestige or credibility group.
   c. On the day of the experiment, appear before Group 1, and explain that you are conducting an experiment to determine the effectiveness of tape-

*Adapted from an experiment reported in Franklyn S. Haiman, "An Experimental Study of the Effects of Ethos in Public Speaking," *Speech Monographs,* Vol. 16 (1949), pp. 190–202. By permission.

recorded speeches. Then, read Introduction 1 to induce a perception of high prestige for the speaker.

d. Play the tape-recorded speech.

e. Administer the Opinion Questionnaire and the Speaker Evaluation Form.

f. Thank the class and instructor, and remove all equipment.

g. Appear before Group 2. Make the same explanation as for Group 1, but read Introduction 2 to induce a perception of low prestige for the speaker.

h. Play the tape-recorded speech; following the speech, administer the Opinion Questionnaire and the Speaker Evaluation Form. Thank the class and instructor, and remove all equipment.

3. Tabulation of the Data

a. Tabulate the number of subjects in each group whose postscores shifted in the direction the speaker advocated, whose postscores shifted away from the position advocated by the speaker, and whose scores did not change.

Subjects	Number	
	Group 1	Group 2
Shifted Toward Speaker		
Shifted Away from Speaker		
Did Not Shift		

b. Calculate the mean scores for each group on both the pre- and post-opinion questionnaires. Compare these mean scores.

	Group 1	Group 2
Preopinion Mean Score		
Postopinion Mean Score		
Difference		

c. Calculate the perceived credibility scores on the Speaker Evaluation Form in the following way:

(1) Score the positive end of each scale as 7 and the negative end as 1. "Competency" is calculated by summing the values circled on the experienced–inexperienced and informed–uninformed scales. "Trustworthy" is calculated by summing the values circled on the just–unjust and honest–dishonest scales. "Dynamism" is calculated by summing the values circled on the aggressive–meek and bold–timid scales.

(2) Arrive at a mean score for each credibility factor (competency, trustworthiness, and dynamism) by dividing the sum of the 2 scales for each factor by 2.

(3) Arrive at an overall credibility score for each subject by summing the means of the 3 credibility factors and dividing by 3.

(4) Arrive at an overall credibility score for each group by summing the scores for each subject and then by dividing by the number of subjects. Record the mean scores for the speech with the high-credibility introduction and the one with the low-credibility introduction.

Factor	Mean Scores	
	Group 1 (High)	Group 2 (Low)
Competency		
Trustworthy		
Dynamism		
Three Factors Combined		

Name _____   Section _____

Date _____   Instructor _____

Results

1. Were Groups 1 and 2 different in terms of their initial opinion toward the topic of the speech? Explain.

2. Which speaker produced the greater amount of shift (in terms of the numbers of individuals who shifted toward the speaker and in terms of degree of shift)?

3. Were there differences between Groups 1 and 2 in terms of how they perceived the prestige or credibility of the speaker?

4. Did a difference occur among scores on the three factors of credibility? That is, did Groups 1 and 2 rate the speaker similarly on any one of the three factors, and did they rate the speaker quite differently on one or more of the factors?

5. Does the way a speaker is introduced seem to have an effect on the way in which an audience reacts to the speech?

Explanation

1. Write a concise summary of this experiment and the results obtained.

2. How do the results of this study answer the research questions?

3. What might be a good way for a speaker to increase the possibility of influencing an audience?

Opinion Questionnaire

Directions: Check the number that most closely matches your opinion on the following issue:

Population control by some form of birth control is a prerequisite for any further advance in human progress.

Strongly Agree ___ : ___ : ___ : ___ : ___ : ___ : ___ Strongly Disagree
                   1   2   3   4   5   6   7

Speaker Evaluation Form

Please indicate your evaluation of the speaker whom you have just heard by checking the number on each scale that most closely represents your feelings.

Experienced ___ : ___ : ___ : ___ : ___ : ___ : ___ Inexperienced
              1   2   3   4   5   6   7

Informed ___ : ___ : ___ : ___ : ___ : ___ : ___ Uninformed
          1   2   3   4   5   6   7

Just ___ : ___ : ___ : ___ : ___ : ___ : ___ Unjust
      1   2   3   4   5   6   7

Honest ___ : ___ : ___ : ___ : ___ : ___ : ___ Dishonest
        1   2   3   4   5   6   7

Aggressive ___ : ___ : ___ : ___ : ___ : ___ : ___ Meek
           1   2   3   4   5   6   7

Bold ___ : ___ : ___ : ___ : ___ : ___ : ___ Timid
        1   2   3   4   5   6   7

Introduction for Group 1 (High-Credibility Speaker)

You are about to hear a recorded speech by the eminent biologist and author Julian Huxley. Dr. Huxley is a professor of zoology and has engaged in research and writing on man and his place in the universe. Dr. Huxley has been Director-General of UNESCO, a United Nations organization, and recently published a book entitled *New Bottles for Old Wine.* The ideas in this speech have been expanded in a book entitled *Our Crowded Planet.* Dr. Huxley is one of the world's truly outstanding experts on the consequences of overpopulation.

Introduction for Group 2 (Low-Credibility Speaker)

You are about to hear a recorded speech by a local used car salesman, Bernard Johnson. Mr. Johnson is a bachelor who read an article on evolution in the *Reader's Digest* last year and has since devoted himself to speaking to service clubs and conventions on the population explosion. He has mimeographed one of his talks, of which this speech is a condensed version. Mr. Johnson was arrested last year for assault and battery on a young fellow whose wife had just given birth to their second child.

Speech for Experimental Stimulus*

Overpopulation is the most serious threat to human happiness and progress in this very critical period in the history of the world. It is not so acute as the threat of atomic warfare, but is graver, since it springs from our own nature.

Thanks to the new vision which we have attained through the knowledge explosion, which has gone on parallel with the population in the last half-century, we have a new vision of our destiny. We may say that today evolution in the person of man is becoming conscious of itself.

I do not want to amplify this at great length. I would remind you, however, that all reality is, in a perfectly genuine sense, evolution; that biological evolution on this planet has been going on for nearly three billion years, and that in the course of that period life has advanced (not only increased in variety, but advanced in organization) so that its highest forms, from submicroscopic pre-cellular units, became cellular, then multicellular, then through hundreds of millions of years grew larger and more powerful with greater control over their environment and greater independence of its changes culminating in land vertebrates and eventually in the latest dominant type, now spread over the whole world—man.

And man is now, whether he likes it or not, and indeed whether he knows it or not (but it is important that he is beginning to know it), the sole agent for the evolutionary process on earth. He is responsible for the future of this planet.

Before we make up our minds what we ought to do in the present crisis, we must try to find what our ultimate aim is as agent or guide of evolution.

Surely, it isn't power. Surely, it isn't just to eat, drink, and be merry, and say, "Well, what's posterity done for us? To hell with posterity!" It isn't just mere quality of possessions or mere quality of people. Nor is it just preparation for some rather shadowy after-life. I would assert that it must be to conserve and to develop the resources of the earth and the resources of our own nature. And so our aim should be to increase the richness of life and enhance its quality.

"Fulfillment" is probably the embracing word; more fulfillment and less frustration for more human beings through greater realization of possibilities. We want more varied and fuller achievement in human societies. We want more variety and less drabness and monotony. We want more enjoyment and less suffering. We want more beauty and less ugliness. We want more adventure and disciplined freedom, as against routine and slavishness. We want more knowledge, more interest, more wonder, as against ignorance and apathy. We want more sense of participation in something enduring and in worthwhile projects, as against a series of competitive rat races, whether with the Russians or our neighbors on the next street.

In the most general terms, we want more transcendence of self in the fruitful development of personality. We want a greater flowering of human dignity and significance, not only as against human degradation, but as against further self-imprisonment in the human ego, and as against mere escapism.

*From *Our Crowded Planet* by Julian Huxley. Copyright © by Julian Huxley 1962. Used by permission of Doubleday & Company, Inc.

Man has been overexploiting the natural resources of this planet. He has been misusing its soils and polluting its waters. He has wasted enormous amounts of resources which he ought to have conserved. Almost everywhere (though mainly in underdeveloped and overpopulated countries), more and more marginal land is being taken into cultivation, more forests are being cut down, more soil erosion is taking place. Everywhere (but in this case especially in the most "developed" countries) high-grade raw materials are being used up at a frightening rate, and lower-grade sources are having to be used. Almost everywhere the supplies of water are becoming insufficient. We are well on the way to ruining our habitat.

Furthermore, not content with destroying or squandering our material resources, we are beginning to destroy our resources of true enjoyment—spiritual, aesthetic, intellectual, emotional. We are spreading great masses of human habitation over the face of the land, neither cities nor suburbs nor towns nor villages, just a vast mass of urban sprawl or subtopia. And to escape from this, people are spilling out farther and farther into the wilder parts and so destroying them. And we are making our cities so big as to be monstrous. They are growing to an impossible size. Just as there is a maximum possible size for an efficient land animal—a land animal more than about twice as large as an elephant could not exist—so there is a maximum possible efficient size for a city. Cities like London, New York, and Tokyo have already got beyond that size.

Looking at the crisis more specifically, mankind is not only proliferating excessively, but increasingly so. In A.D. 1600 the total number of people in the world was only about half a billion. It first reached 1 billion at about the end of the nineteenth century. By 1950 it had passed 2 billion. Today it is 2¾ billion, and increasing by nearly 50 million a year. Every twenty-four hours it increases by over 140,000—the equivalent of a good-sized town; and every minute by about 100—the equivalent of ten baseball teams complete with coaches.

What is more, the *rate* of increase is itself increasing. Before the discovery of agriculture, it must have been below one-tenth of one percent per annum; it reached one percent only at the beginning of the present century, but by now stands at over 1½ percent, and is still going up.

Still worse, the increase is very unevenly distributed over the world. By far the highest increase is in the underdeveloped countries with the lowest standard of life, notably in Asia and Latin America. This is bad for several reasons. In the first place, it makes their development much more difficult. To develop an underdeveloped country to an industrial and social level where it can hold its own in the modern world and give its people a reasonable standard of life, needs a great deal of capital, technical skill, and trained manpower. If too many babies are born, too much of that capital and skill and manpower will be used up in providing food, housing, education, health, and other services for them, and will not be available for economic and technological development. Coale and Hoover, in their careful study of the problem, concluded that if India did not reduce its birth rate by about 50 percent in the next thirty-five or forty years it would never be able to break through from its state of underdevelopment and underemployment to a developed and developing industrially based economy; on the contrary, it would reach a point of no return, after which living standards would go down instead of up. And the same general conclusion applies to other countries, such as Pakistan or Indonesia, with a high density of population at a low economic standard of life.

Then there is, as everyone knows, a great gap between the average standards of life in developed and underdeveloped areas—between the haves and have-nots. Thus the average real income of the 200 million people of North America is nearly twenty-five times as high as that of the over 1,600 million people of Asia, and the disparity in energy available to an inhabitant of the United States and India is even higher. The existence of this huge gap produces jealousy and unrest, and has generated what has been called the Revolution of Expectation in the have-not countries—an expectation of aid which must at all costs be satisfied.

The bridging of this gap is linked with the population problem. To take the Indian example again, at the moment, though the production of food is just keeping up with the production of people, it will not be able to go on doing so unless the rate of population increase slows down. Furthermore, a large proportion—about three-quarters, according to the Food and Agriculture Organization—of the people in underdeveloped countries is undernourished—in plain words, not getting enough of the right food to eat—and increased food production must aim at satisfying this deficiency too. And about the same proportion is grossly undereducated—in plain words, illiterate. Finally, the economic gap is widening instead of narrowing—the rich countries are getting richer, the poor countries getting poorer.

Attempts to bridge the gap by aid and assistance to underdeveloped nations are eminently desirable, and indeed necessary, if we are to have a peaceful and prosperous world. However, as I have just pointed out, all the science and goodwill in the world cannot find a way of successfully industrializing a densely populated and underdeveloped country if its increase rate is too high.

In the long run the key to the problem is the reduction of the human birth rate. In the present century medical science, in conjunction with improved conditions of life, has markedly reduced the world death rate, but without any appreciable reduction in the birth rate. It has brought about what we may call "death control" on a world scale: The contemporary population explosion is the result. It is now necessary to supplement worldwide death control with worldwide birth control. Population control, by some form of birth control, is a prerequisite for anything that can be called progress or advance in human evolution, even in the immediate future. One major contribution that science can make is the discovery of better and simpler methods of birth control. The time has now come for the world and all its nations to think seriously about population policy.

Experiment 8.2
Attractiveness and Desire to Influence

Proposition

Persuaders tend to be more effective if they are viewed as physically attractive by those they are trying to persuade.

Research Questions

Is a physically attractive communicator more effective than an unattractive one?

Are people persuaded by someone who appeals to them very much and who openly and honestly informs them that he or she wants to change their opinions?

Research Methods*

Subjects

Four groups of 10 to 20 individuals each consisting of approximately 75% males and 25% females; 15 males and 5 females would be an acceptable group.

One female confederate who is willing to appear in an attractive and an unattractive condition. The confederate should be the same for all 4 groups.

Two male experimenters to administer the questionnaires.

Materials

Preexperimental Opinion Questionnaire on issues of relevance to college students, but with 5 items (3, 8, 14, 18, 19) on general versus specialized education (1 copy for each subject).

Opinion Questionnaire on general versus specialized education but with only five items (6, 7, 8, 9, 10) to be compared to the Preexperimental Opinion Questionnaire (1 copy for each subject).

Personality Rating Form (2 copies for each subject).

Procedures
1. Selection of Subjects, Confederates, and Experimenters
   a. The actual subjects in this study are male students; the female students are involved in order to make the presence of the female confederate plausible. Subjects should be selected from sections of a large, basic course in speech, psychology, or sociology. They should come from their different sections to a central room. Arrange with the instructors at least one month prior to the experiment to have 2 or 3 students from 5 to 7 different sections participate in the experiment.

Adapted from an experiment reported in Judson Mills and Elliot Aronson, "Opinion Change as a Function of the Communicator's Attractiveness and Desire to Influence," *Journal of Personality and Social Psychology*, Vol. 1 (1965), pp. 173–177. Copyright 1965 by the American Psychological Association. By permission.

b.   A highly attractive female confederate should be enlisted to participate as the persuader. In the attractive condition, she should wear stylish, tight-fitting clothing; her hair should be modish; and she should wear becoming makeup. In the unattractive condition, she should be made to look unpleasant. She should wear loose, ugly, ill-fitting clothing; her hair should be messy; her makeup should be conspicuously absent and her complexion somewhat oily and unwholesome looking. Assistance from the drama department may be secured in preparing the confederate.

2.   Conduct of the Experiment

a.   At least 2 weeks prior to the experimental sessions, arrange with the instructors to administer the Preexperimental Opinion Questionnaire to all students in their sections as part of the regular class activities. Collect the questionnaires for use at a later time. The 5 items dealing with general versus specialized education will be used to measure opinion change later.

b.   There will be four experimental sessions. Session 1 (group 1) should be the first session held. Session 1 will measure reaction to attractiveness with persuasion. Session 2 will measure reaction to unattractiveness without persuasion. Session 3 will measure reaction to attractiveness without persuasion. Session 4 will measure reaction to unattractiveness with persuasion. In terms of time, these sessions should be held as close together as possible. However, do not run them simultaneously.

c.   When the subjects arrive at the experimental session, Experimenter 1 should explain that he is conducting a study to find out how students feel about the issue of general versus specialized education. He should state that he would like them to complete a questionnaire on this topic but that the results will be much more valid if respondents are allowed to think about the questions before responding. He should state that in order to familiarize everyone with the questions, he is going to have one person in the group give his or her answers aloud in front of everybody.

d.   In the *persuade condition* (Sessions 1 and 4), Experimenter 1 should ask for a volunteer to answer each question in the questionnaire aloud. The female confederate should volunteer and be chosen. In the *nonpersuade condition* (Sessions 2 and 3), Experimenter 1 should say that he has had difficulty in getting volunteers in the past, and so he is going to pick someone himself. He should choose the confederate, who should always be seated near the front of the room. The confederate should appear reluctant to participate but should finally agree to do so.

e.   For Session 1, the confederate should be made up attractively and use the persuade condition response; that is, to questions 6–10 in the Opinion Questionnaire on general versus specialized education, the confederate should answer, "Very much."

f.   For Session 2, the confederate should be made up unattractively and use the nonpersuade condition response; that is, to questions 6–10, she should respond, "Not at all."

g.   For Session 3, the confederate should be made up attractively and use the nonpersuade condition response.

h. For Session 4, the confederate should be made up unattractively and use the persuade response.

i. For each session, Experimenter 1 should read each item, have the confederate respond, then allow the subjects to make their responses to that item. This procedure should be followed for all the 15 items.

j. As soon as subjects have responded to all the 15 items, Experimenter 1 should explain that since the questionnaire has not taken the full time, the remaining time will be spent on another study. Experimenter 2 should enter the room and be introduced; then Experimenter 1 should leave.

k. Experimenter 2 should explain that he is interested in finding out how much people agree in their ratings of someone after they have seen him or her briefly. He should distribute the Personality Rating Form and ask the subjects to rate Experimenter 1, who has just left. He should explain that their ratings will be kept confidential.

l. As soon as they finish, dismiss the female confederate, and ask the subjects to rate the confederate in order to find out how much people agree in their ratings of someone after they have seen him or her briefly.

m. After completing their ratings of the female confederate, Experimenter 2 should ask subjects to turn over the rating forms and describe their reactions to the experiment in a few sentences. Those subjects whose comments indicate suspicion of the procedure may be eliminated from the analysis.

n. Experimenter 2 should caution the subjects not to discuss the experiment in order to avoid biasing future results.

3. Tabulation of the Data

a. Tally the scores for all the subjects in the prequestionnaire on the 5 items (3, 8, 14, 18, 19) on general versus specialized education. Divide the subjects' scores into the 4 groups, and calculate the mean score for each of the 4 groups.

b. Tally the scores for each subject on the 5 items in the postquestionnaire on general versus specialized education, and calculate the mean score for each of the 4 groups.

	Attractive						Unattractive					
	Persuade (Session 1)			Nonpersuade (Session 3)			Persuade (Session 4)			Nonpersuade (Session 2)		
Items	Pre	Post	Diff	Pre	Post	Diff	Pre	Post	Diff	Pre	Post	Diff
1												
2												
3												
4												
5												

c. Tally the scores on the Personality Rating Form for each of the 4 groups on the characteristics "attractive," "beautiful," "timid," and "opinionated," and calculate the means for each group.

	Attractive		Unattractive	
	Persuade (Session 1)	Nonpersuade (Session 3)	Persuade (Session 4)	Nonpersuade (Session 2)
Attractive				
Beautiful				
Timid				
Opinionated				

Name _____   Section _____

Date _____   Instructor _____

Results

1. In which condition was the confederate viewed as most attractive?

2. In which condition was the confederate most persuasive?

3. In which condition was the confederate viewed as most timid and most opinionated?

4. What influence, if any, does an attractive person have on opinion change?

5. Does stating a desire to influence or persuade others seem to have a positive or detrimental effect on opinion change?

Explanation

1. Write a concise summary of this experiment and the results obtained.

2. How does making a statement that you want to influence a person's opinions affect how the person views your attractiveness?

3. Using the data obtained, what suggestions would you give to a political candidate about how to make the most effective use of people who speak for the candidate?

Preexperimental Opinion Questionnaire

We are interested in what college and university students feel about a number of social issues. We are sure that you have thought about and discussed many of these issues and have received information about them through newspapers, television, and various courses in the humanities, education, and the social sciences. The statements that make up this survey cover many points of view. You will probably find yourself agreeing with some statements, disagreeing with others, and perhaps neutral about still others. There are no "right" or "wrong" answers; the best answer is *your personal opinion*. You can be sure that, whatever your opinion may be on a certain issue, many people will agree with you while others will disagree.

Please read each statement carefully, and check the scale according to your first reaction. It is not necessary to take a lot of time for any one question.

Directions: (1) Read the question, and decide upon your answer. (2) Place a check-mark above the appropriate number. (3) Please be sure to answer every item.

1. One can't tell much about a person's character by his appearance.

Strongly Agree ___ : ___ : ___ : ___ : ___ : ___ : ___ Strongly Disagree
  1   2   3   4   5   6   7

2. Obedience and proper respect for authority should be the very first requirements of a good citizen.

Strongly Agree ___ : ___ : ___ : ___ : ___ : ___ : ___ Strongly Disagree
  1   2   3   4   5   6   7

3. Every college student should receive a broad general education.

Strongly Agree ___ : ___ : ___ : ___ : ___ : ___ : ___ Strongly Disagree
  1   2   3   4   5   6   7

4. Some leisure is necessary, but it is good, hard work that makes life interesting and worthwhile.

Strongly Agree ___ : ___ : ___ : ___ : ___ : ___ : ___ Strongly Disagree
  1   2   3   4   5   6   7

5. A bright person usually cannot do mechanical things well.

Strongly Agree ___ : ___ : ___ : ___ : ___ : ___ : ___ Strongly Disagree
  1   2   3   4   5   6   7

6. Students who arrive at college with deficiencies in basic English and mathematics should be rejected.

Strongly Agree ___ : ___ : ___ : ___ : ___ : ___ : ___ Strongly Disagree
  1   2   3   4   5   6   7

7. Rather than being a place to get educated, the university campus is a circumscribed environment for stalking a socially acceptable mate.

Strongly Agree ___ : ___ : ___ : ___ : ___ : ___ : ___ Strongly Disagree
1   2   3   4   5   6   7

8. Students should not be forced to take courses to make them well rounded.

Strongly Agree ___ : ___ : ___ : ___ : ___ : ___ : ___ Strongly Disagree
1   2   3   4   5   6   7

9. Persons of only slightly superior intelligence can expect to graduate from most colleges if they expend enough time in study.

Strongly Agree ___ : ___ : ___ : ___ : ___ : ___ : ___ Strongly Disagree
1   2   3   4   5   6   7

10. Grades in courses are the only evidence of education that counts.

Strongly Agree ___ : ___ : ___ : ___ : ___ : ___ : ___ Strongly Disagree
1   2   3   4   5   6   7

11. The motivation that impels college students to join fraternities and sororities is fear of being assessed solely on their individual merits.

Strongly Agree ___ : ___ : ___ : ___ : ___ : ___ : ___ Strongly Disagree
1   2   3   4   5   6   7

12. Politicians talk principles but practice compromise.

Strongly Agree ___ : ___ : ___ : ___ : ___ : ___ : ___ Strongly Disagree
1   2   3   4   5   6   7

13. Books and movies ought not to deal so much with the unpleasant and seamy side of life as they ought to concentrate on themes that are entertaining or uplifting.

Strongly Agree ___ : ___ : ___ : ___ : ___ : ___ : ___ Strongly Disagree
1   2   3   4   5   6   7

14. The real potentialities of the human personality are fully realized only through the development provided by a general education.

Strongly Agree ___ : ___ : ___ : ___ : ___ : ___ : ___ Strongly Disagree
1   2   3   4   5   6   7

15. Educational institutions have been the most effective groups in fighting prejudice and discrimination.

Strongly Agree ___ : ___ : ___ : ___ : ___ : ___ : ___ Strongly Disagree
1   2   3   4   5   6   7

16. Fraternities and sororities, which base membership on religious affiliation, nationality, or race, should not be allowed to exist on our campus.

Strongly Agree ___ : ___ : ___ : ___ : ___ : ___ : ___ Strongly Disagree
1   2   3   4   5   6   7

17. Criminals, especially those guilty of sex crimes, should have mental and medical help rather than severe punishment.

Strongly Agree $\frac{}{1}$: $\frac{}{2}$: $\frac{}{3}$: $\frac{}{4}$: $\frac{}{5}$: $\frac{}{6}$: $\frac{}{7}$ Strongly Disagree

18. Technical training should not be part of the offerings at a university.

Strongly Agree $\frac{}{1}$: $\frac{}{2}$: $\frac{}{3}$: $\frac{}{4}$: $\frac{}{5}$: $\frac{}{6}$ $\frac{}{7}$ Strongly Disagree

19. The true objective of a university is to develop the ideals of a democratic life rather than to train people in automotive mechanics and secretarial skills.

Strongly Agree $\frac{}{1}$: $\frac{}{2}$: $\frac{}{3}$: $\frac{}{4}$: $\frac{}{5}$: $\frac{}{6}$: $\frac{}{7}$ Strongly Disagree

20. The true American way of life is disappearing so fast that force may be necessary to preserve it.

Strongly Agree $\frac{}{1}$: $\frac{}{2}$: $\frac{}{3}$: $\frac{}{4}$: $\frac{}{5}$: $\frac{}{6}$: $\frac{}{7}$ Strongly Disagree

21. The object of education is the development of the whole person in relationship to other whole persons; thus, specialized and fragmentary information fails to find a central place in higher education.

Strongly Agree $\frac{}{1}$: $\frac{}{2}$: $\frac{}{3}$: $\frac{}{4}$: $\frac{}{5}$: $\frac{}{6}$: $\frac{}{7}$ Strongly Disagree

22. Parents' actions, not formal education, are probably the most important influence in forming a child's character.

Strongly Agree $\frac{}{1}$: $\frac{}{2}$: $\frac{}{3}$: $\frac{}{4}$: $\frac{}{5}$: $\frac{}{6}$: $\frac{}{7}$ Strongly Disagree

23. Universities should provide separate classes for very bright students.

Strongly Agree $\frac{}{1}$: $\frac{}{2}$: $\frac{}{3}$: $\frac{}{4}$: $\frac{}{5}$: $\frac{}{6}$: $\frac{}{7}$ Strongly Disagree

24. With such a heavy emphasis on scientific advances, the truly liberating and humanizing subjects such as English, philosophy, the arts, languages, and history are being slighted, to the detriment of the purpose of a university.

Strongly Agree $\frac{}{1}$: $\frac{}{2}$: $\frac{}{3}$: $\frac{}{4}$: $\frac{}{5}$: $\frac{}{6}$: $\frac{}{7}$ Strongly Disagree

25. Both women and men will attain their potential best when they treat each other as equals.

Strongly Agree $\frac{}{1}$: $\frac{}{2}$: $\frac{}{3}$: $\frac{}{4}$: $\frac{}{5}$: $\frac{}{6}$: $\frac{}{7}$ Strongly Disagree

Opinion Questionnaire on General Education

We are interested in what college students feel about the issue of general versus specialized education.

Directions: (1) Read each question carefully, and decide upon your answer. (2) Place a checkmark above the appropriate number. (3) Please be sure to answer every item.

1. To what extent would you like to get other students to agree with you on this issue?

Very Much ___ : ___ : ___ : ___ : ___ : ___ : ___ Not at All
             1   2   3   4   5   6   7

2. How interested are you in this issue?

Very Much ___ : ___ : ___ : ___ : ___ : ___ : ___ Not at All
             1   2   3   4   5   6   7

3. How much thought have you given to this issue?

Very Much ___ : ___ : ___ : ___ : ___ : ___ : ___ Not at All
             1   2   3   4   5   6   7

4. To what extent would you like to get more information about this issue?

Very Much ___ : ___ : ___ : ___ : ___ : ___ : ___ Not at All
             1   2   3   4   5   6   7

5. To what extent would you like to know the views of others on this issue?

Very Much ___ : ___ : ___ : ___ : ___ : ___ : ___ Not at All
             1   2   3   4   5   6   7

6. Every college student should receive a broad general education.

Strongly Agree ___ : ___ : ___ : ___ : ___ : ___ : ___ Strongly Disagree
                 1   2   3   4   5   6   7

7. Students should not be forced to take courses to make them well rounded.

Strongly Agree ___ : ___ : ___ : ___ : ___ : ___ : ___ Strongly Disagree
                 1   2   3   4   5   6   7

8. The real potentialities of the human personality are fully realized only through the development provided by a general education.

Strongly Agree ___ : ___ : ___ : ___ : ___ : ___ : ___ Strongly Disagree
                 1   2   3   4   5   6   7

9. Technical training should not be part of the offerings at a university.

Strongly Agree ___ : ___ : ___ : ___ : ___ : ___ : ___ Strongly Disagree
        1   2   3   4   5   6   7

10. The true objective of a university is to develop the ideals of a democratic life rather than to train people in automotive mechanics and secretarial skills.

Strongly Agree ___ : ___ : ___ : ___ : ___ : ___ : ___ Strongly Disagree
        1   2   3   4   5   6   7

11. Preparation in logic and reasoned discourse is more important in a university education than salesmanship and accounting.

Strongly Agree ___ : ___ : ___ : ___ : ___ : ___ : ___ Strongly Disagree
        1   2   3   4   5   6   7

12. A specialized education is antithetical to the objectives of a liberal, humane university education.

Strongly Agree ___ : ___ : ___ : ___ : ___ : ___ : ___ Strongly Disagree
        1   2   3   4   5   6   7

13. Specialization leads to narrower and narrower perspectives in which students know more and more about less and less.

Strongly Agree ___ : ___ : ___ : ___ : ___ : ___ : ___ Strongly Disagree
        1   2   3   4   5   6   7

14. A person who can converse on the arts and great books can make a greater contribution to the maintenance of a great culture than a technical specialist can.

Strongly Agree ___ : ___ : ___ : ___ : ___ : ___ : ___ Strongly Disagree
        1   2   3   4   5   6   7

15. The idea of a university is to prepare people who can cope with the great problems of mankind, not the technicalities of day-to-day trivialities.

Strongly Agree ___ : ___ : ___ : ___ : ___ : ___ : ___ Strongly Disagree
        1   2   3   4   5   6   7

Personality Rating Form

Directions: Rate the person on each personality characteristic listed below. Circle the number that best indicates how well each characteristic applies to the person being rated. That is, if the characteristic applies extremely well to the person, circle the number 15; if the characteristic is extremely inappropriate, circle the number 1.

Charming	1	2	3	4	5	6	7	8	9	10	11	12	13	14	15
Fashionable	1	2	3	4	5	6	7	8	9	10	11	12	13	14	15
Timid	1	2	3	4	5	6	7	8	9	10	11	12	13	14	15
Anxious	1	2	3	4	5	6	7	8	9	10	11	12	13	14	15
Attractive	1	2	3	4	5	6	7	8	9	10	11	12	13	14	15
Exuberant	1	2	3	4	5	6	7	8	9	10	11	12	13	14	15
Conceited	1	2	3	4	5	6	7	8	9	10	11	12	13	14	15
Frank	1	2	3	4	5	6	7	8	9	10	11	12	13	14	15
Beautiful	1	2	3	4	5	6	7	8	9	10	11	12	13	14	15
Vain	1	2	3	4	5	6	7	8	9	10	11	12	13	14	15
Superficial	1	2	3	4	5	6	7	8	9	10	11	12	13	14	15
Likable	1	2	3	4	5	6	7	8	9	10	11	12	13	14	15
Emotional	1	2	3	4	5	6	7	8	9	10	11	12	13	14	15
Neat	1	2	3	4	5	6	7	8	9	10	11	12	13	14	15
Modest	1	2	3	4	5	6	7	8	9	10	11	12	13	14	15
Annoying	1	2	3	4	5	6	7	8	9	10	11	12	13	14	15
Unpleasant	1	2	3	4	5	6	7	8	9	10	11	12	13	14	15
Romantic	1	2	3	4	5	6	7	8	9	10	11	12	13	14	15
Shy	1	2	3	4	5	6	7	8	9	10	11	12	13	14	15
Candid	1	2	3	4	5	6	7	8	9	10	11	12	13	14	15
Cynical	1	2	3	4	5	6	7	8	9	10	11	12	13	14	15
Frank	1	2	3	4	5	6	7	8	9	10	11	12	13	14	15
Affectionate	1	2	3	4	5	6	7	8	9	10	11	12	13	14	15
Lively	1	2	3	4	5	6	7	8	9	10	11	12	13	14	15
Vivacious	1	2	3	4	5	6	7	8	9	10	11	12	13	14	15
Honest	1	2	3	4	5	6	7	8	9	10	11	12	13	14	15
Opinionated	1	2	3	4	5	6	7	8	9	10	11	12	13	14	15
Modest	1	2	3	4	5	6	7	8	9	10	11	12	13	14	15

Chapter 9
Small Group Factors

The beliefs, feelings, and attitudes of an individual are anchored in the groups to which the person belongs; that is, groups tend to influence how an individual behaves. Any attempt to change individual behavior can be facilitated or deterred by pressures associated with group membership. When an individual's behavior is changed toward that of a group standard as a result of real or imagined group influence, we say that the individual is *conforming* to the group. As individuals influence one another in groups, they eventually become more and more like each other in attitude and action. The result is that groups become somewhat uniform in what they consider acceptable behavior. People who fail to behave consistently with the standards of acceptable behavior established by a group are called *nonconformists*.

The experiments that follow attempt to examine differences in productivity and opinion change that occur as a result of group pressures and participation. Additional evidence of the strength of group influence on individual behavior can be gained through your personal observation of the kinds of decisions made by your friends and acquaintances. You might want to look for the influence of group membership on some of your own decisions.

Experiment 9.1
Individual vs. Group Judgment

Proposition
Small groups tend to influence individuals because the product of group problem solving is usually considered superior to that of the average individual working alone.

Research Questions
Do groups of people solve problems more accurately and quickly than individuals working alone?

Do groups of people who are equally informed and talented perform better than talented individuals working alone?

Research Methods*

Subjects
Sixty individual volunteers or 2 classes of 30 students. Eight groups of 5 individuals will be *experimental* subjects, and the remaining 20 students will be *control* subjects.

Materials
One copy of each form (A and B) of the Bradley Formal Validity in Problem Solving Test for each subject.

Procedures
1. Selection of the Subjects
   a. Administer Form A of the Formal Validity in Problem Solving Tests, along with the answer sheet (to be provided by your instructor), to all 60 subjects. Instruct them to work out the solutions to the 30 problems individually. Subjects should be given 50 minutes to complete the test items.
   b. Score each test, and rank the subjects according to the total number of items answered correctly.
   c. Create 8 homogeneous groups by placing 5 individuals who received the same or somewhat similar scores on the test in the same group.
2. Conduct of the Experiment
   a. Anywhere from one week to one month later, give each of the 8 experimental groups copies of the alternate form of the test (Form B), and instruct each group to reach a group decision by consensus on each of the 30 problems. Each group should be given 50 minutes to complete the test.
   b. Give the 20 control subjects Form B of the test, and ask them to complete it individually during the 50-minute period of time.
   c. When all the subjects have completed the tests, debrief them. Hold a discussion with the experimental subjects concerning the factors they felt influenced their performance as members of a group.
3. Tabulation of the Data
   a. Determine majority decisions for 40 experimental subjects on Form A by taking individual answers for each of the 30 items on Form A and identifying which items receive a majority of the answers. That will be the majority response.

---

*Adapted from an experiment reported in Dean C. Barnlund, "A Comparative Study of Individual, Majority, and Group Judgment," *Journal of Abnormal and Social Psychology,* Vol. 58 (1959), pp. 55–60. Copyright 1959 by the American Psychological Association. By permission.

	Experimental Group					
	No. Subjects Marking Each Alternative					
Problem	a	b	c	d	e	Majority Choice
1						
2						
3						
4						
5						
6						
7						
8						
9						
10						
11						
12						
13						
14						
15						
16						
17						
18						
19						
20						
21						
22						
23						
24						
25						
26						
27						
28						
29						
30						

b. Tally the number of correct answers scored by each individual on Form A. For each experimental group calculate an experimental group majority score by taking the five individual scores (number of correct answers) on Form A for each group and getting the average score of the correct answers for each group; for group consensus scores, tally the number of correct answers for each experimental group on Form B.

No. of Correct Answers		
Individuals (Form A)	Majority (Form A)	Consensus (Form B)
1	Grp 1	Grp 1
2	2	2
3	3	3
4	4	4
5	5	5
6	6	6
7	7	7
8	8	8

Continue to include all 60 subjects.

c. Calculate the mean number of correct answers for all individual subjects for the majority decisions and for the group consensus decisions.

	Mean No. of Correct Answers
Individual	
Majority	
Consensus	

d. Calculate the mean scores of correct answers for control subjects on Forms A and B.

	Control Group Mean Scores
Form A	
Form B	

Name _____   Section _____

Date _____   Instructor _____

Results

1. Which group had the higher mean scores: The control group? Individuals working alone? Majority decisions? Group consensus?

2. How do group consensus scores (Form B) compare with the scores (Form A) of the highest scoring individual in each group.

3. In small groups, is majority rule likely to be the best way of arriving at decisions? Why?

4. What seem to be the most serious barriers to getting higher scores in the consensus condition? Why didn't consensus groups score higher?

5. Do the results of this study indicate that time per se facilitates or hinders the kinds of decisions made? That is, both individuals and groups had 50 minutes to complete the test. Would it be more desirable to give a group of five individuals 250 minutes since an individual working alone has 50 minutes? Why?

Explanation

1. Write a concise summary of this experiment and the results obtained.

2. Which research questions were answered by this study and which ones were not? Explain.

Bradley Formal Validity in Problem Solving Test (Form A)*

Recognition of Valid Conclusions

Directions: Below are listed partially constructed arguments. The "material validity" or "truth" of the information in the two given statements is to be accepted. The question is simply this: Granting the accuracy of the information given, which of the conclusions follows? You are to select that conclusion which you think follows logically from the given statements and to indicate your choice by circling the appropriate letter. Examine the sample below very carefully before you begin the test.

Example: An examination of the records shows that *every* member of the committee voted for the proposal. John Doe is a member of the committee. Therefore: (a) The proposal was adopted unanimously. (b) All members were in favor of the proposal. (c) John Doe voted for the proposal. (d) The records were probably wrong. (e) None of the conclusions follows.

You will note the letter *c* has been circled, indicating that the correct answer is *c*: *John Doe voted for the proposal.* Follow this same procedure for all the exercises.

1.   All socialists are antagonistic to free enterprise. All who advocate socialized medicine are socialists. Therefore: (a) Socialists are undesirable. (b) Socialized medicine is undesirable. (c) Democracy must be preserved at all costs. (d) All who advocate socialized medicine are antagonistic to free enterprise. (e) None of these conclusions follows.

2.   All those who believe in ghosts are ignorant and superstitious. John Doe does not believe in ghosts. Therefore: (a) The first premise in this syllogism is obviously false because some very brilliant people believe in ghosts. (b) We need more and better education to cope with inherited superstitions. (c) John Doe is not ignorant and superstitious. (d) No one who is ignorant and superstitious doubts that ghosts exist. (e) None of these conclusions follows.

3.   No one of average intelligence doubts the existence of a Deity or Supreme Being. All atheists doubt the existence of a Deity or Supreme Being. Therefore: (a) Preventing atheism should be one of the chief aims of modern education. (b) No atheists possess average intelligence. (c) The first premise is false; because an individual does not believe in God, he is not necessarily feebleminded. (d) Some of those who doubt the existence of a Deity are not atheists. (e) None of these conclusions follows.

4.   All members of fraternities are university students. Some members of fraternities are habitual drinkers. Therefore: (a) Some university students are not habitual drinkers. (b) Some habitual drinkers are not university students. (c) Some habitual

*Reprinted here by permission of the late Dr. Earl E. Bradley.

drinkers are university students. (d) Fraternities are detrimental to college life. (e) None of these conclusions follows.

5. All zebras wear stripes. All prisoners wear stripes. Therefore: (a) Some zebras are prisoners. (b) All zebras are prisoners. (c) All prisoners are not zebras. (d) All zebras are not prisoners. (e) None of these conclusions follows.

6. Some communists are advocates of heavy taxes. All advocates of heavy taxes are conservative Republicans. Therefore: (a) Some advocates of heavy taxes are not communists. (b) Some communists are conservative Republicans. (c) Some conservative Republicans are communists. (d) Some communists are not advocates of heavy taxes. (e) None of these conclusions follows.

7. No tax which discourages investment is a good tax. All taxes on personal and corporate income discourage investment. Therefore: (a) No tax on personal or corporate income is a good tax. (b) Taxes on personal income do not discourage investment as much as taxes on corporate income. (c) Income taxes should be revised so that they will not discourage investment. (d) Although taxes do discourage investment, they are good taxes because they tax those who are able to pay. (e) None of these conclusions follows.

8. All those who are elected to public office are professional politicians. No conscientious and honest individual is a professional politician. Therefore: (a) Some of those who are elected to public office are not honest and conscientious men. (b) Some professional politicians are not elected to public office. (c) No conscientious and honest individual is elected to public office. (d) It is the responsibility of the American voter to be more discriminating in his choice of candidates. (e) None of these conclusions follows.

9. Some college football teams are "passing teams" since their attack depends on the forward pass. All college football teams use the "T." Therefore: (a) Teams which use the single wing are not passing teams. (b) Some college football teams are not passing teams. (c) Some passing teams do not use the "T" formation in the backfield. (d) Some teams which use the "T" are passing teams. (e) None of these conclusions follows.

10. All good Americans vote according to the dictates of their conscience. Howard voted for the socialist candidate. Therefore: (a) Howard is not a good American. (b) Howard should have studied government when he was in school. (c) Howard voted as his conscience told him, and actually he is a good American. (d) Howard probably doesn't have a conscience. (e) None of these conclusions follows.

11. All doctors are opposed to socialized medicine. No opponents of socialized medicine are "liberals." Therefore: (a) All doctors are "conservatives." (b) Those who oppose socialized medicine are "conservatives." (c) No "liberals" are doctors. (d) Some of those opposed to socialized medicine are not doctors. (e) None of these conclusions follows.

12. All communists are advocates of violence. No advocates of violence are Republicans. Therefore: (a) Advocates of violence should be treated as traitors. (b) No

Republicans are communists. (c) No advocates of violence are communists and Republicans. (d) No Republicans are advocates of violence. (e) None of these conclusions follows.

13.   No communists are desirable citizens. No desirable citizens advocate violence. Therefore: (a) Some communists advocate violence. (b) Some communists do not advocate violence. (c) Some communists are desirable citizens. (d) Communists are Russian and enemies of the U.S. (e) None of these conclusions follows.

14.   All of the celestial bodies that revolve around the sun are planets rather than stars. Mars, which can be plainly distinguished by its reddish gleam, revolves around the sun. Therefore: (a) Mars is closer to the earth than any other planet. (b) Mars must have heavy deposits of some mineral which causes it to shine with a reddish glow. (c) Mars is a member of the same solar system as in the earth. (d) Mars is a planet rather than a star. (e) None of these conclusions follows.

15.   No idealists are atheists. Some optimists are atheists. Therefore: (a) Some atheists are not optimists. (b) Some optimists are not idealists. (c) No idealist is an optimist. (d) No atheists are optimists. (e) None of these conclusions follows.

16.   No members of the Republican party support an increase. Senator X is not a member of the Republican party. Therefore: (a) Senator X is a member of the Democratic party. (b) Some Democrats oppose tax increases as well as Republicans. (c) Senator X does not support tax increases. (d) Senator X supports tax increases. (e) None of these conclusions follows.

17.   Some Americans are not well-informed citizens. All Americans read their newspapers continually. Therefore: (a) The newspapers should do a better job of writing news stories. (b) The average American is not a proficient reader. (c) Some well-informed citizens do not read their newspapers continually. (d) Some who read their newspapers continually are not well-informed citizens. (e) None of these conclusions follows.

18.   No Ethiopians are Bantus. Some Bantus are Africans. Therefore: (a) Some Africans are not Bantus. (b) All Ethiopians are Africans. (c) Some Africans are not Ethiopians. (d) Some Ethiopians are not Africans. (e) None of these conclusions follows.

19.   Some who visit Russia are converted to communism. Some professors at this college have visited Russia. Therefore: (a) Some professors at this college are converts to communism. (b) All Russians are not communists. (c) All professors are not communists as a result of having visited Russia. (d) Professors should not visit Russia as communism is very undesirable. (3) None of these conclusions follows.

20.   No mechanics have artistic talents. Some mechanics are excellent craftsmen. Therefore: (a) Some excellent craftsmen do not have artistic talents. (b) Some excellent craftsmen are not mechanics. (c) Some mechanics are not excellent craftsmen. (d) Some who have artistic talent are excellent craftsmen. (e) None of these conclusions follows.

21.   All communists are advocates of violence. Some Republicans are not advocates of violence. Therefore: (a) No Republican is a communist. (b) No Republican is an advocate of violence. (c) Some Republicans are not communists. (d) No advocates of violence are communists and Republicans. (e) None of these conclusions follows.

22.   All communists are believers in heavy taxes. All my opponents are believers in heavy taxes. Therefore: (a) All my opponents are communists. (b) My opponents are not all communists. (c) Some of my opponents are communists. (d) Communists are undesirable since they believe in heavy taxes. (e) None of these conclusions follows.

23.   No poor students at College X are football players. Some who attend College X are poor students. Therefore: (a) Some who attend College X are not football players. (b) Some football players are poor students. (c) No football players are good students. (d) All football players at College X are good students. (e) None of these conclusions follows.

24.   All ministers are educated men. Some ministers are not hypocrites. Therefore: (a) Some hypocrites are educated men. (b) Some educated men are hypocrites. (c) Some ministers are hypocrites. (d) All hypocrites are educated men. (e) None of these conclusions follows.

25.   Some Eskimos live north of the Arctic Circle. All people who live north of the Arctic Circle subsist chiefly on seal and fish. Therefore: (a) All those who live north of the Arctic Circle are Eskimos. (b) All those who live chiefly on seal and fish are Eskimos. (c) All Eskimos subsist chiefly on seal and fish. (d) No one who lives south of the Arctic Circle subsists on seal and fish. (e) None of these conclusions follows.

26.   All ladies speak in a low, well-modulated voice. All ladies are courteous and considerate of others. Therefore: (a) All who are courteous and considerate of others speak in low, well-modulated voices. (b) All who speak in low, well-modulated voices are courteous and considerate of others. (c) Some who speak in low, well-modulated voices are courteous and considerate of others. (d) Some who are courteous and considerate of others have low, well-modulated voices. (e) None of these conclusions follows.

27.   All college professors are well educated. All professional men are well educated. Therefore: (a) All college professors are professional men. (b) Some college professors are professional men. (c) Some professional men are college professors. (d) Some well-educated men are neither college professors nor professional men. (e) None of these conclusions follows.

28.   No Polynesians are poor swimmers. All Polynesians are brown-skinned. Therefore: (a) No poor swimmers are brown-skinned. (b) Some poor swimmers are not brown-skinned. (c) Some brown-skinned people are not poor swimmers. (d) Some brown-skinned people are not Polynesians. (e) None of these conclusions follows.

29. No athletes are stupid. All stupid people have inferiority complexes. Therefore: (a) No athletes have inferiority complexes. (b) Some who have inferiority complexes are not athletes. (c) Some who have inferiority complexes are not stupid. (d) None who have inferiority complexes are athletes. (e) None of these conclusions follows.

30. All who cannot read are illiterate. All illiterates are lacking in intelligence. Therefore: (a) No one who is lacking in intelligence can read. (b) Some who are lacking in intelligence are not illiterate. (c) Some who are lacking in intelligence cannot read. (d) No illiterate can read. (e) None of these conclusions follows.

Bradley Formal Validity in Problem Solving Test (Form B)*

Recognition of Valid Conclusions

Directions: Below are listed partially constructed arguments. The "material validity" or "truth" of the information in the two given statements is to be accepted. The question is simply this: Granting the accuracy of the information given, which of the conclusions follows? You are to select that conclusion which you think follows logically from the given statements and to indicate your choice in the appropriate place on the answer sheet. Examine the sample below very carefully before you begin the test.

Example: An examination of the records shows that every member of the committee voted for the proposal. John Doe is a member of the committee. Therefore: (a) The proposal was adopted unanimously. (b) All members were in favor of the proposal. (c) John Doe voted for the proposal. (d) The records are probably wrong. (e) None of the conclusions follows.

You will note that on your answer sheet the letter c has been circled, indicating that the correct answer is *c: John Doe voted for the proposal.* Follow this same procedure for all the exercises.

1.   All members of the Mongoloid races are Asiatic. All Buddhists are members of the Mongoloid race. Therefore: (a) Some Asiatics are neither Buddhists nor Mongoloid. (b) All Asiatics are Buddhists. (c) Some members of the Mongoloid race are not Buddhists. (d) All Buddhists are Asiatic. (e) None of these conclusions follows.

2.   All football players at College X are given board and room. Some students at College X are not football players. Therefore: (a) Football players are entitled to special consideration. (b) Some students at College X are not given room and board. (c) Some football players earn far more than they ever receive from the school. (d) In order for a college to have a good football team, it is necesary to give players special consideration. (e) None of these conclusions follows.

3.   No good citizens fail to vote on an election day. All hospitalized invalids fail to vote on election day. Therefore: (a) No hospitalized invalids are good citizens. (b) Some good citizens are not hospitalized invalids. (c) The premise that all good citizens vote obviously means that all good citizens who are able will vote and thus excludes invalids, who are not able to go to the polls. (d) Some of those who fail to vote are not hospitalized invalids. (e) None of these conclusions follows.

4.   All those who give false information on their income tax questionnaires are criminals. Some good citizens who don't understand complicated tax forms give

*Reprinted here by permission of the late Dr. Earl E. Bradley.

false information on their income tax questionnaires. Therefore: (a) Some good citizens who do not understand tax forms are criminals. (b) The government should simplify its tax forms. (c) All criminals give false information on their income tax forms. (d) Some good citizens are not criminals. (e) None of these conclusions follows.

5. All great orators must be familiar with the subjects upon which they speak. Senator Richard Roe is invariably familiar with the subjects on which he speaks. Therefore: (a) Senator Roe is a good orator. (b) Senator Roe will be a great orator if he keeps plugging away. (c) Senator Roe works hard and deserves to be re-elected. (d) Since Senator Roe does know what he is talking about, he is an exceptional legislator. (e) None of these conclusions follows.

6. Some Americans are conscientious objectors in time of war. All conscientious objectors in time of war are considered good citizens. Therefore: (a) Some poor citizens are not conscientious objectors in time of war. (b) Some poor citizens are Americans. (c) Some Americans are not conscientious objectors in time of war. (d) All poor citizens are conscientious objectors in time of war. (e) None of these conclusions follows.

7. No members of the Democratic party are opposed to civil liberties. All Southern Senators are members of the Democratic party. Therefore: (a) No Southern Senators are opposed to civil liberties. (b) Most Southern Senators are opposed to civil liberties. (c) Some Southern Senators are not opposed to civil liberties. (d) Both premises are false and do not state facts. (e) None of these conclusions follows.

8. All those who are advocates of high protective tariff are Republicans. No Democrats are Republicans. Therefore: (a) Some Republicans are not Democrats. (b) Some of those who advocate a high protective tariff are not Democrats. (c) Big business' domination of the Republican party is responsible for the Republican's attitude on the protective tariff. (d) No Democrats are advocates of a high protective tariff. (e) None of these conclusions follows.

9. Some of the men students at College X are members of fraternities. All of the men students at College X are members of R.O.T.C. Therefore: (a) All members of fraternities are members of R.O.T.C. (b) Some members of R.O.T.C. are members of fraternities. (c) All members of fraternities are men students at College X. (d) Some men students at College X are not members of fraternities. (e) None of these conclusions follows.

10. All gentlemen are men. Some men are not gentlemen. Therefore: (a) Some men are gentlemen. (b) All men should be gentlemen. (c) One can be both a man and a gentleman at the same time. (d) If an individual is spoken of as a "man" he is, in all probability, a gentleman. (e) None of these conclusions follows.

11. All Kansas schools admit blacks on an equal basis with whites. No blacks are admitted on an equal basis with whites in Southern schools. Therefore: (a) Blacks actually have the same education as whites. (b) Southern discrimination against

blacks is deplorable. (c) Some schools which admit blacks on an equal basis with whites are not Southern schools. (d) No Southern school is a Kansas school. (e) None of these conclusions follows.

12. No geniuses have well-balanced personalities. Some of our greatest music composers were undeniably geniuses. Therefore: (a) A well-balanced personality is not necessary for great artistic achievement. (b) No one with a well-balanced personality can hope to be a successful composer. (c) Some of our greatest musical composers did not have well-balanced personalities. (d) Nature has a law of compensation—to those who haven't a well-balanced personality, she gives great intelligence or artistic ability. (e) None of these conclusions follows.

13. No men of low morals and weak character can be a good public official. Richard Roe is not a man of low morals and weak character. Therefore: (a) Richard Roe can be a very good public official. (b) Richard Roe can be a very good public official if he is not lazy. (c) Richard Roe cannot be any kind of public official until he is elected to office. (d) All candidates for public office should be required to take an examination which would determine what kind of character and morals each candidate possesses. (e) None of these conclusions follows.

14. All members of the Republican party are opposed to higher taxes. Some senators are members of the Republican party. Therefore: (a) The Republican party has always opposed higher taxes. (b) High taxes are bad for the individual and for business. (c) Some senators are opposed to higher taxes. (d) Some Republicans are senators. (e) None of these conclusions follows.

15. No debaters at College X are poor students. Some of those who attend College X are poor students. Therefore: (a) Actually, no students at College X are debaters. (b) Some of those who attend College X are not debaters. (c) No debaters at College X ever flunked a course. (d) Some of those who attend College X are not poor students. (e) None of these conclusions follows.

16. Some of the people who do not believe in God are atheists. Some philosophers do not believe in God. Therefore: (a) Some philosophers are atheists. (b) All those who do not believe in God are either atheists or philosophers, or both. (c) Philosophy should not be taught in our public schools since it creates more atheists. (d) The church should reconcile Christian religion with all philosophies. (e) None of these conclusions follows.

17. Some members of the Republican party are not capitalistic. No members of the Republican party are opposed to higher taxes. Therefore: (a) The Republican party has always opposed high taxes. (b) Some Republicans are capitalists. (c) Some of those opposed to high taxes are not capitalists. (d) Some capitalists are not opposed to high taxes. (e) None of these conclusions follows.

18. No one who believes in the U. S. Constitution is a socialist. Some socialists are good citizens. Therefore: (a) Prejudice toward the Socialist party is unjust. (b) Some socialists are not good citizens. (c) Some good citizens are not socialists. (d) Some good citizens do not believe in the U. S. Constitution. (e) None of these conclusions follows.

19.   Some of the nations of the Near East are Moslem nations. Syria is not a Moslem nation. Therefore: (a) Syria is one of the countries in the Near East which is not a Moslem nation. (b) The Crusades were responsible for keeping Mohammedanism out of Syria for this long. (c) Since Syria is surrounded by Moslem nations, it cannot remain Christian for very long. (d) Syria is not located in the Near East at all. (e) None of these conclusions follows.

20.   No "liberals" are opposed to federal aid to education. Some "liberals" are members of the Republican party. Therefore: (a) Some members of the Republican party are not opposed to federal aid to education. (b) Some "liberals" are not Republicans. (c) All "liberals" are in favor of federal aid to education. (d) Some of those opposed to federal aid to education are not Republicans. (e) None of those conclusions follows.

21.   All post office employees are bonded. James is not bonded. Therefore: (a) James is a post office employee. (b) James is not a post office employee. (c) James should be bonded like all the other postal employees, as it protects the public interest. (d) James is not bonded because the postal officials trust him. (e) None of these conclusions follows.

22.   All Republicans are advocates of a high protective tariff. No Democrats are Republicans. Therefore: (a) Republicans and Democrats differ on this issue. (b) I believe that the Republicans are wrong. (c) No Democrats are advocates of a high protective tariff. (d) I believe that the Democrats are wrong. (e) None of these conclusions follows.

23.   No communists are desirable citizens in a democracy. Some who live in this country are avowed communists. Therefore: (a) All communists should be deported. (b) Communists should not be allowed to teach in our schools. (c) Those who do not appreciate democracy should be denied its privileges and opportunities. (d) Some who live in this country are not desirable citizens. (e) None of these conclusions follows.

24.   All gypsies are born dancers. Some born dancers do not have slow reflexes. Therefore: (a) All born dancers are gypsies. (b) Some gypsies have slow reflexes. (c) Some gypsies dance as poorly as anyone else. (d) Some with slow reflexes are gypsies. (e) None of these conclusions follows.

25.   No French are very stable in temperament. Some Europeans are not French. Therefore: (a) No Europeans are very stable in temperament. (b) All who are stable emotionally are Europeans. (c) No one who is stable in temperament is French. (d) All Europeans are very persevering. (e) None of these conclusions follows.

26.   All ministers are persuasive speakers. All ministers are religious men. Therefore: (a) All persuasive speakers are religious men. (b) All religious men are persuasive speakers. (c) Some who are ministers are also persuasive and religious. (d) Some religious men are persuasive speakers. (e) None of these conclusions follows.

27.   No Texans are timid. All Texans are cowboys. Therefore: (a) Some timid people are not cowboys. (b) Some cowboys are not Texans. (c) Some cowboys are not timid people. (d) No cowboys are timid. (e) None of these conclusions follows.

28.   All Negroes are underprivileged. All racial minorities are underprivileged. Therefore: (a) Some underprivileged may not be Negroes. (b) All Negroes are members of a racial minority. (c) Some Negroes are members of a racial minority. (d) Some members of racial minorities are Negroes. (e) None of these conclusions follows.

29.   No one who is destitute buys U.S. savings bonds. All who buy U.S. bonds are good citizens. Therefore: (a) No one who is destitute is a good citizen. (b) Some good citizens do not buy U.S. savings bonds. (c) No good citizens are destitute. (d) Some good citizens are not destitute. (e) None of these conclusions follows.

30.   All burros are beasts of burden. All beasts of burden are faithful. Therefore: (a) All faithful beasts are beasts of burden. (b) Some faithful beasts are neither beasts of burden nor burros. (c) Some faithful beasts are burros. (d) All faithful beasts are burros. (e) None of these conclusions follows.

Experiment 9.2
Conformity

Proposition

The small group influences the behavior of its members by setting standards for acceptable ways of behaving by rewarding those who conform and by punishing those who deviate from them.

Research Questions

Does an individual who is attracted to a group but who deviates from its well-defined group norm tend to change his or her opinion toward the group norm?

Is an individual who communicates his or her opinion a lot more than another individual responding to pressures toward changing the group norm?

Does an increased possibility of being rejected for nonconformity create pressures to change toward the group norm?

Research Methods*

Subjects

Forty-eight individuals divided into 4 groups—all homogeneous with respect to sex and class status and all cohesive with respect to interest in the same subject.

Materials

Copy of the Johnny Sandron case for each subject (48 copies).

Three copies of the Opinion Continuum and the Personal Responsibility Scale for each subject (144 copies).

Copy of Outline for writing descriptions for each subject (48 copies).

Postexperimental Questionnaire for each subject (48 copies).

Procedures

1. Selection and Preparation of Subjects
   a. Secure permission to select subjects from several sections of a basic course in psychology, sociology, speech, or communication.
   b. Select subjects by asking for volunteers who would like to participate in a group discussion about human relations and social problems. This can be done by means of a short questionnaire in which the students indicate their name, sex, and class standing (Fr., Soph., Jr., Sr., Grad.) and check one of the following topics they would be interested in talking about in a group discussion:

*Adapted from an experiment reported in Bertram H. Raven, "Social Influence on Opinions and the Communication of Related Content," *Journal of Abnormal and Social Psychology*, Vol. 58 (Jan. 1959), pp. 119–128. Copyright 1959 by the American Psychological Association. By permission.

Architecture and the environment

Human relations and social problems

Mental development and genetics

Medicine and inflation

Use only subjects who check "Human relations and social problems."

   c.   Assign subjects to groups of the same sex and class status (male freshmen, female freshmen, etc.). Secure 4 groups of 12 individuals each. Number the groups 1, 2, 3, and 4.

2.   Conduct of the Experiment

   a.   Locate the groups out of hearing distance from one another, and ask them to discuss the effects of poor human relations on juvenile delinquency. Stop the discussions after 5 minutes.

   b.   Give each subject a copy of the Johnny Sandron case to read.

   c.   When the initial reading has been completed, distribute the Opinion Continuum and one copy of the Personal Responsibility Scale to each subject. Stress that their opinions will be private and that only the experimenter will see the scales.

   d.   As soon as the subjects have indicated their opinions on the 7-point scale, collect them. Explain to Groups 1 and 4 (rejection condition) that since it was important that members of the group get along well together, they will have an opportunity to reorganize the group in order to exclude those members with whom they could not get along especially well. Tell these 2 groups that they will soon receive ballots on which they can indicate who should leave. Tell them that the 3 individuals with the most votes will be asked to leave and take part in another research project. Explain to Groups 2 and 3 (nonrejection condition) that all members of each group will remain for the entire session.

   e.   With the scales in hand, privately report to each group a fictitious consensus of responses by saying the following:

You are probably curious about how others in this group think about the extent to which Johnny is responsible for his crime. Therefore, I shall place on the blackboard the number of people who have chosen each position. I shall indicate this with X's so that it will not be necessary to identify each person specifically.

Regardless of the actual scale positions, list the following on the blackboard:

Scale Position	Frequency
1	xxxxxx
2	xx
4	x
5	x
6	x
7	x

f. Explain to all the subjects that later each group will be asked to write a separate group report on the case, much as social workers do, but that they must all agree completely on the report. Indicate that a prize will be awarded to the group which submits the best report. Tell subjects that with this report in mind, they are to read the case again.

g. As soon as all the subjects have reread the case, administer the Personal Responsibility Scale again. Stress again the private nature of the responses.

h. Collect the scales, and inform the subjects that as an aid to preparing to write their group report, they are individually to write a description of the case as they see it. Explain to Groups 2 and 4 (public condition) that the individual descriptions will be passed around so that all other members of their group can see them; and to facilitate distribution of their individual reports, they will be taken away to be xeroxed. Indicate to Groups 1 and 3 (private condition) that the individual descriptions will not be seen by anyone but the experimenter. Distribute copies of the Outline to assist all subjects in the 4 groups in organizing the description.

i. Give subjects 10 minutes to complete their individual descriptions; then collect them, and administer the Personal Responsibility Scale again.

j. Collect the scales, and administer the Postexperimental Questionnaire.

k. Collect the Postexperimental Questionnaires, and debrief the subjects (that is, explain why they did not eliminate people from their groups and did not write up a group report).

3. Tabulation of the Data

a. Tally the scores for each subject on the 3 administrations of the Personal Responsibility Scale.

Subjects	Scale Position		
	Adm. 1	Adm. 2	Adm. 3
Group 1 1			
2			
3			
4			
5			
6			
7			
8			
9			
10			

Follow the above pattern for all four groups.

b. Determine the number of deviates in each group. Do this by comparing the fictitious consensus distribution that was put on the blackboard with the positions chosen by the subjects on the initial scale. All subjects who initially occupied positions 5, 6, or 7 are called the *deviates*. All subjects who initially occupied positions 2, 3, or 4 are called the *modes*—that is, they were consistent with the fictitious consensus and hence in the apparent majority. Report the data below.

| | Distribution of Subjects in Experimental Conditions | | | |
| | Public | | Private | |
	Modes	Deviates	Modes	Deviates
Rejection				
Nonrejection				

c. Tally the number of subjects, according to the experimental condition, who indicated on the Postexperimental Questionnaire (question 1) that they felt that their opinions would affect the degree to which they might be rejected by the group.

| | Likelihood of Rejection | | | | | | |
	1	2	3	4	5	6	7
Public Deviates							
Public Modes							
Private Deviates							
Private Modes							

d. Tally the number of subjects, according to the experimental condition, who indicated on the Postexperimental Questionnaire (question 5) that their first opinions differed from that of the group.

| | First Opinion Differed from Group | | | | | | |
	1	2	3	4	5	6	7
Public Deviates							
Public Modes							
Private Deviates							
Private Modes							

e. Tally the number of deviates who changed opinions *toward* the group norm.

	Public	Private	Combined
Rejection			
Nonrejection			
Combined			

f. Tally the number of modes and deviates who changed their opinions, either toward or away from the group norm.

	Initial Position	Changed Toward 1	Did Not Change	Changed Toward 7
Modes				
Deviates				

g. Tally the number of deviates changing 1, 2, 3, and 4 steps toward Position 2 (the norm) on the scale.

Initial Position	No. of Positions Changed			
	1	2	3	4
5				
6				
7				

h. Tally the number of individual descriptions that are consistent with Position 2 (the norm) on the scale. Separate them into groups, indicating those that moved after writing the descriptions.

	No. of Deviates Changing Opinions While Writing Descriptions			
	Position Before Change			
	1	2	3	4
Public				
Private				

Name _____ Section _____

Date _____ Instructor _____

Results

1. How many subjects changed their opinions from the initial scale position to the final position?

2. Which group of subjects changed more: Private modes? Private deviates? Public modes? Public deviates?

3. Which subjects in the initial Positions 5, 6, or 7 changed the most?

4. Did the possibility of rejection seem to influence the amount of change?

5. Were the experimental conditions achieved? That is, did some subjects feel rejected and thus in fact deviate from the group norm?

6. Does communicating about a subject tend to exert pressure toward conformity?

Explanation

1. Write a concise summary of this experiment and the results obtained.

2. What do the results of this study reveal about the research questions?

3. If you wanted to increase the amount of pressure toward conformity with group norms, what methods are suggested by this study?

The Case of Johnny Sandron

Johnny was arrested for the robbery-murder of an aged, eccentric spinster, Miss Luella Barlow. A coroner's report revealed that Miss Barlow had been stabbed from behind, receiving deep gashes about the head, neck, and back. A bloody eight-inch bowie knife, carefully wiped to remove fingerprints, was found nearby. Also found was Miss Barlow's purse with the change purse removed. Evidence indicated that the victim had died after one of the very first wounds but had been stabbed a number of times afterwards.

Johnny was immediately suspected and was picked up by a police squad car about three hours later as he was walking out of a neighborhood theater. He had just seen an Abbott and Costello comedy. Johnny still had some money in his pocket. He had carefully washed blood stains from his clothing, but there was still enough evidence of blood to make his guilt quite evident. He confessed readily, then wept freely, saying that he hadn't meant to hurt her.

Johnny and His Environment

At the age of 15, Johnny was two years older than the average child in his seventh grade class and had a record of truancy and disinterest. He left school several months before the crime.

Johnny, his mother, and a younger brother, David, lived in a one-room flat in one of the worst slum areas in town. Six years ago his father had taken to drink and had died a year ago in a drunken brawl. During the past few years, Mrs. Sandron had attempted to supplement the scanty Welfare Department funds with what she could earn by taking in washing. John contributed some by selling magazines. Johnny's brother, David, aged 13, is anemic, a victim of congenital syphilis. David has a very high IQ and has shown considerable promise in school. An elder brother, "Lippy," has been in prison for some time now for a second sentence of armed robbery—the victim of the armed robbery was stabbed but managed to recover.

Interview Material

Note: The following are summary interviews made up by an investigating social case worker. In composing them, several concessions have been made to clarity and the time element in this study. The questions asked by the social worker have been omitted and the interview material put together so that it reads more smoothly. Less relevant parts of the interviews have been omitted. However, we have attempted to preserve the essential flavor and the pertinent facts from each interview.

Interview with Mrs. Sandron

At heart, Johnny was a good boy but always felt that he wasn't wanted and was doing things all the time to make us think he was important. Thomas (Mr. Sandron) didn't care what happened to the kids. He never spent any time with the kids like other fathers do—except when he hit them, like when he was drunk. Johnny used to imitate his father when he would beat up small kids in the neighborhood. Johnny never liked Lippy and he was ashamed of him—said that Lippy was just a cheap crook. When the cops came for Lippy, Johnny said to me, "Good for Lippy. That's what he should get. He deserves it."

. . . Johnny used to get mad at David. He was jealous of David on account of David always got better clothes and food. I used to buy candy for David because the doctor said he needed sugar, but I couldn't afford to give any to Johnny. Johnny knew David was sick and needed these things, yet sometimes when my back was turned, he would beat up David and take candy and things away from him.

. . . He wanted to look dirty and tough. I tried to do better for the boys, but I didn't get much money, and lots of times I would look in the sugar bowl where I kept it and it would be gone—stolen.

. . . Johnny didn't have a bad nature. He never did anything wrong before this. He used to work hard selling magazines, and he would give me the money he got. He liked birds and animals, and he used to get mad when kids would tie tin cans to cats. Other kids in the neighborhood couldn't understand this. They laughed at him because he liked birds and called him "Sparrow." They called him "yellow" because he wouldn't steal. He had to learn to steal because it was what he had to do to get along with his friends. Once he organized a bunch of smaller kids to play baseball and play games. He said he wanted to help them. Some of the boys stole, but Johnny used to hit them if he caught them and make them give the things back.

. . . In school, Johnny was a terror. He always picked on the other smaller kids —trip them, put gum in their hair. They all said that he was a big bully. The kids' mothers used to come to me crying, ask me to do something about "Sparrow." The people at school tried to understand him. They used to come out and talk to me about him and ask me what they could do. Whatever they did, it didn't seem to make Johnny any better. Even the school psychologist gave Johnny up and said that he didn't know what you could do with him—seems like he was just bad. Johnny didn't try—he was too busy trying to be tough. We tried for a while to put him in a trade school to learn metal and woodwork—maybe he just didn't do good in booklearning. No use. He gave everybody there so much trouble that he was expelled. Johnny never did anything right, and everytime he failed he got worse —he tried to make up for his failures by acting tough.

. . . The night she (Luella) was killed, Johnny came home early and asked me where was his bowie knife. He said he was going somewhere to get some money. Luella was a kind old lady, but people didn't understand her. She always used to do things for people—used to give kids candy and she never bothered anyone.

. . . Johnny heard me say that day that I just had to have some money to get David his medicine and didn't know how I could get it. He said I would get it somehow. . . .

Interview with Johnny's Teacher—Miss Smith

Johnny was always a trial to his teachers. He was nervous, fidgety, sullen, obstinate, cruel, disobedient, and disruptive. Teachers could only stand him for one day at a time. He is the most difficult boy I have ever had. I don't believe he belongs in a classroom. There is nothing in which he is interested enough to apply himself. From his very first day, he would enter the room sneering and disrupt the classroom. He would smoke, swagger, and use foul language continually. His attitude was reflected by his slovenly dress and appearance. Johnny had no regard for what belonged to anybody else. He would always rip everything out of the hands of others, continually bullying the children who were younger and smaller than he. He would pick fights and take sadistic pleasure in torturing the children and hurting them. The other children could not help hating him. He had no friends.

. . . We have generally tried to understand Johnny. Mr. Jones, the principal, has had any number of conferences with me, with other teachers, and with the school psychologist. We have tried to do everything to help Johnny to adjust to school better, but his obstinacy has always gotten the better of us. Even the police came and consulted with us. They had tried being nice to him, letting him go with a warning when he was caught stealing. It had not done any good. Whenever there has been anything wrong—a child hurt, something stolen from the cloakroom—we have always known where to look for the culprit—Johnny was always found to be responsible.

. . . Johnny's behavior carried beyond school. He often stole money and goods from neighborhood stores, newsstands, as well as from neighbors. In his neighborhood he had organized a number of smaller boys who were a terror in the neighborhood. The gang was broken up when Johnny led them in a stoning attack on a settlement house.

. . . Johnny was friendless in school and at home. Often he would attempt to use his stolen articles to attempt to buy friendship.

. . . He became more and more violent. This culminated in an attack on a smaller boy which was so vicious that the child had to be hospitalized. To protect the children and for the good of all concerned, Johnny was asked to leave school.

In his home relations, Johnny showed considerable hatred for his mother. Mrs. Sandron worked hard to support the two boys, particularly David—a charming and brilliant boy—who was ill. She showed considerable love and affection for Johnny, too, always tried to do what she could for him. In return, Johnny often struck her and would often stay away from home for extended periods without letting her know where he was. Johnny also despised his brother David, considered him a "pantywaist" and a bookworm. He was once heard remarking to one of his friends that he would be happy if David "kicked off already." Johnny's ideal was his older brother, a habitual criminal. When his brother was convicted of "armed robbery" and "assault with intent to kill," Johnny cursed the "cops." He seemed to want to be like his older brother more than anything else.

Some of the people in the neighborhood felt that Luella Barlow "had it coming to her." She had been mean to Johnny. She used to hire Johnny to do odd jobs for her and then not pay him, strike him when he objected . . . . The murder would seem to be deliberate: Johnny had often told younger children that he was going to kill her some day, but that he felt he would want her to die slowly so that "she would feel it." The very day of the crime, I heard him tell a little girl that he would take her to the movies that night and that he knew where he would get the money for it.

Interview with Johnny
Sure I'm glad I did it. And I would do it again, too. I enjoyed seeing her get it after all the things she did to me and the other kids. She was always mean to me and to the other kids. I guess she was nice to me once in a while. She gave me dinner

lot of times when I didn't have anything to eat at home. And she gave me money more than once just when I told her I needed it. She even stopped some of the big boys from down the street from beating me up once. Then she sticks her nose where it wasn't wanted—like the time she hit me for feeding poisoned birdseeds to the pigeons. She used to buy things we stole—said that was just to help us out . . . but she never paid us much . . . still owed me for the watch I stole from that drunk and lots of other things too. When I was walking home that night, she called me. . . . Why don't I come up and see her anymore, she asks. I said cause she still owed me for things and besides I was going straight. She looks at me and smiles.

. . . She was against me just like everybody else. My teachers, the other kids, the cops, even my mother and brothers. All of them were against me—nobody liked me. Okay for them. If they want war, they'll get it. . . . The cops always used to pull me in when they didn't have a thing on me because I didn't do nothing . . . they always say, "We know you. You are no good like your old man and your brother Lippy. You might as well confess cause we'll have you in the pen in no time." They never give me a chance. Sure I used to steal . . . peaches from the orchard, cakes from the bakery, money from drunks, then stuff from stores. I had a gang that had them going for a while. Most of the kids were younger, but they could steal like nobody's business—I taught them. They did everything they shouldn't do in school, and we practically burned down the school once. I really got a charge out of that—it makes you feel like you really got something when you got a gang behind you that does what you say.

In school I used to see the teacher and the principal talking about me . . . say how they could make me less trouble for them, or should they kick me out of school altogether . . . never how they could help me with anything. . . . Anything wrong, it was always my fault. First thing I go into the room, teacher says in front of the kids, "You're Johnny Sandron. I know all about you. But don't think you're not going to be good in here!" . . . Most of the kids in the room were little and weak. I used to enjoy seeing them wince when I hit them. Luella was weak too. Some of them used to pay me once a month I shouldn't hit them. . . . I would have stuck at school, 'cept that David was sick and Mom needs money. . . . Hadda quit to find a job. Had to help out David. He needed medicine right away bad. Wanted to do what I could to help him get well. He was a right kid—always did the right thing.

. . . You think my family sticks up for me? Not on your life. My old lady never did like me—always used to slap me . . . said she never wanted me in the first place. I would do anything for her. The money I got from stealing I would never give her—only the money I got right. She didn't get much money from me—I lost what I made in magazines at Joe's Pool Room—Lippy had the right idea. He sure knew how to put one over on the cops. I could get along OK if I had Lippy's guts.

The Opinion Continuum

Considering the good and bad features of Johnny's basic personality and behavior and of the world in which he lived, as well as the nature of the crime, to what extent do you think Johnny is personally responsible for his crime and to what extent should his environment be considered responsible?

1. Johnny had many decent influences of which he could have taken advantage. The conditions under which he lived were friendly enough so that they can hardly be held responsible for his misdeeds. *The blame for his crime must be placed entirely upon his shoulders.*

2. Though Johnny may have been slightly influenced by the harmful conditions under which he lived, there were also many helpful factors to counterbalance them. He did not take advantage of these. Considering this, it seems that by far *the greatest part of the blame* still *rests on his shoulders.*

3. There were many helpful influences even if harmful ones were present, and *it is still Johnny who is blameworthy for his crime and behavior in light of this.*

4. Johnny had both helpful and disturbing influences. *The blame for his crime must be placed equally both on Johnny and on conditions in which he lived.*

5. Johnny did have helpful influences, but more that encouraged crime and delinquency. Johnny's behavior was at times praiseworthy. Thus, though Johnny should be held responsible for his crime to some extent, *more of the blame rests not on his shoulders but upon the conditions in which he lived.*

6. Johnny never really had much of a chance. Though there was some slight choice left to him, so that he might be held responsible to some small degree, the general situation in which Johnny found himself contributed infinitely more to his becoming a criminal. In light of this, together with the many good aspects of his behavior, *we must consider Johnny as largely a victim of his circumstances.*

7. Considering the terrible conditions under which Johnny lived, it would seem almost a miracle that he didn't come out worse than he did. In spite of everything, Johnny's behavior was still essentially good. *Not he but his environment is entirely to blame for his misdeeds.*

Personal Responsibility Scale

Check the one number that most nearly represents your opinion on the extent to which Johnny's environmental conditions or he, personally, should be considered responsible for the commission of the crime.

#		
1.		Johnny Responsible
2.	Environment Responsible	Johnny Responsible
3.	Environment Responsible	Johnny Responsible
4.	Environment Responsible	Johnny Responsible
5.	Environment Responsible	Johnny Responsible
6.	Environment Responsible	Johnny Responsible
7.	Environment Responsible	

Outline

On the two general topics below, write anything which you consider pertinent to a completely factual description of the case. Concentrate on including all the facts in these areas; avoid recommendations or opinions.

Description of the Crime

Here you may want to include such things as a description of the crime itself, Johnny's motives, the victim, her relationship to Johnny, his attitude toward the crime, etc.

Johnny's Relationship to Others

Here you may want to include such things as a description of Johnny's treatment by others, his treatment of others, his family, his school—his teachers and playmates—the police, etc.

Postexperimental Questionnaire

Directions: Circle the letter opposite the statement that most closely represents your feelings about the question.

1. How much did you feel that your opinion (as to whether Johnny or his environment was responsible) would affect the degree to which the others in the group would prefer to have you continue working with them on the case study?

Not at All ___ : ___ : ___ : ___ : ___ : ___ : ___ Definitely Affect

           1   2   3   4   5   6   7

2. What possibility is there that the other members of the group will find out how you personally (privately) feel about this case study?

Not at All
Possible ___ : ___ : ___ : ___ : ___ : ___ : ___ Definitely Possible

           1   2   3   4   5   6   7

3. How likely is it that the others in the group would prefer that you not continue working with them?

Not at All ___ : ___ : ___ : ___ : ___ : ___ : ___ Definitely

           1   2   3   4   5   6   7

4. What is the possibility that your opinion about the case will be the basis for others not wanting to continue working with you?

Not at All ___ : ___ : ___ : ___ : ___ : ___ : ___ Definitely

           1   2   3   4   5   6   7

5. How much did your first opinion differ from that of the group as a whole?

Completely ___ : ___ : ___ : ___ : ___ : ___ : ___ Not at All

           1   2   3   4   5   6   7

Chapter 10
Social Action Factors

Social action is the process by which change is produced in a large social structure, such as a group of professionals like doctors, a community, or a government body like a county. The people who instigate the action are called *change agents*. The major objective of social action is to get people to adopt new ideas, practices, products, and ways of thinking. Change produced by individual factors and decisions or by small groups is part of the total process by which innovative practices are adopted. But social action involves decisions by larger institutions and necessitates concerted action among several formal groups, ranging from a neighborhood, town, county, state, or even a nation. Advertising campaigns, United Fund drives, equal opportunity movements, and government reform programs are examples of attempts at social action.

Research on social action has often involved extensive field investigations that require large numbers of researchers and huge amounts of money. Recently, however, a number of laboratory-controlled experiments have been conducted to test aspects of social action on a smaller scale. The first experiment in this chapter, for example, describes an investigation of the purchase or adoption of a food product in an apartment complex. With some minor changes, you should be able to conduct this experiment in an area in your community.

Experiment 10.1
Two-Step Flow in Marketing

Proposition
Although the communication media arouse interest in new actions, interpersonal communication is especially influential in the actual decision to adopt.

Research Questions
Do impersonal sources of information influence opinion leaders more than non-leaders?

Does word-of-mouth information flow more often from leaders to nonleaders than in the opposite direction?

Do people who get favorable information by word-of-mouth tend to buy new products more often than those who get unfavorable word-of-mouth information?

Are later (in the three-week period) buyers more likely to receive information by word-of-mouth than early buyers?

Research Methods*

Subjects
Residents of an apartment building, dormitory, or student housing area to whom a letter and coupon can be sent for buying a new product at a special price from a grocery store, drug store, or student bookstore, whose customers are primarily from that complex.

A retail merchant who agrees to offer a *new brand* of a commonly purchased product, such as toothpaste, lotion, soap, or something regularly purchased by customers.

Materials
A letter and a coupon from either the manufacturer of the product or from the merchant offering the product will be sent to the residents for redemption within 3 weeks of receipt of the coupon; a line for residents to sign and date when they redeem the coupon should be provided.

A standard Interview Guide for interviewing subjects.

Procedures
1. Selection of Subjects and Stimulus Materials
   a. Locate a housing area where residents tend to shop at a local store and where they seem fairly homogeneous, such as a married-student housing area.
   b. Contact a merchant whom the residents tend to patronize or a store where they could shop easily, and secure his or her agreement to participate in the study.
   c. Assist in the selection of a new brand of a product and in the preparation of a letter and coupon to be sent to the residents.
2. Conduct of the Experiment
   a. Have the letter and coupon mailed to residents near the beginning of the month, making the offer for a period of 3 weeks.
   b. At closing time each day, collect the coupons redeemed, and prepare a list of purchasers, addresses, and telephone numbers to use in scheduling interviews.

*Adapted from an experiment reported in Johan Arndt, "A Test of the Two-Step Flow in Diffusion of a New Product," *Journalism Quarterly,* Vol. 45 (1968), pp. 457–465. By permission.

c. Arrange an interview with each person who redeemed a coupon and purchased the product.

d. Interview each person by asking the questions in the order listed in the guide and recording answers on the guide. Classify anyone receiving two or more choices as Opinion Leaders (that is, whose names were written two or more times on the Interview Guide).

3. Tabulation of Data

a. Separate out the Opinion Leader coupons from the others, and prepare a table indicating the number of Opinion Leaders in each time-of-adoption category (see 3-e).

	Opinion Leaders	Nonopinion Leaders	Totals
Innovators			
Early Adopters			
Early Majority			
Late Majority			
Laggards			
Nonadopters			
Totals			

b. Identify who talked to whom about the product by tabulating the responses to the questions, "Did you talk to anyone about the coupon offer?" "Who?" "Did (name) contact you or did you contact her/him?" "Did the conversation occur before or after you purchased the product?" "What aspects of the offer were discussed (letter and coupon or use of product, etc.)?" "Did you consider the comments as favorable or unfavorable to the product?" Tabulate the responses according to Opinion Leader, Nonleader, and Nonadopter.

c. What is the total number of households in the housing unit?

_____ No. of Households

d. Tabulate the number of coupons redeemed on each day of the week, and total them.

	Week 1	Week 2	Week 3	Totals
Monday				
Tuesday				
Wednesday				
Thursday				
Friday				
Saturday				
Sunday				
Totals				

e. Tabulate all the adopters according to the time-of-adoption categories.

	No. Adopting
Innovators (first two days)	
Early Adopters (3rd to 7th day)	
Early Majority (8th to 12th day)	
Late Majority (13th to 16th day)	
Laggards (17th to 21st day)	
Nonadopters (did not redeem coupon)	

f. Identify the Opinion Leaders by making a list of individuals mentioned in response to question 9, "When you want information about a product that you have not tried yet, who in this housing unit do you usually ask? Please list three people in order of priority, if possible."

g. Tabulate the data by going to questions 5 and 6 in the Interview Guide.

| | Word-of-Mouth Contacts and Purchase Time | | | | |
| | Initiated | | Received | | |
	Before	After	Before	After	Totals
Opinion Leader					
Nonleader					
Nonadopter					
Totals					

h. Tabulate the data by going to questions 7 and 8 in the Interview Guide.

| | Content of Conversation | | | | | | |
| | Letter and Coupon | | Use of Product | | Other | | |
	Favor.	Unfav.	Favor.	Unfav.	Favor.	Unfav.	Totals
Opinion Leader							
Nonleader							
Nonadopter							
Totals							

Results

1. Of the total number of households receiving the letter and coupon, how many purchased the product?

Calculate the percentage of the total who purchased the product.

How many subjects purchased the product *prior* to engaging in a conversation with someone?

What does that data reveal about the impact of direct mailing?

2. How many subjects purchased the product without contacting someone else for an opinion?

What is the percentage of those who contacted someone else and then purchased the product as compared with those who purchased but did not contact someone?

What do the percentages indicate with respect to word-of-mouth communication?

3. Who was more influenced by the impersonal source (letter and coupon), the Opinion Leaders or the Nonleaders? The Early Majority or the Laggards?

What factors might explain that influence?

4. Who initiated the largest number of word-of-mouth contacts?

Which group of adopters received the largest number of word-of-mouth contacts?

How would the flow of information between Leaders and Nonleaders be characterized?

5. Where were the identified Opinion Leaders located among the time-of-adoption categories?

6. What kind of influence did the content of the conversations seem to have on adoption (purchase of the product)?

Did the favorableness of the comments toward the product seem to influence purchasers?

Explanation

1. Write a concise summary of this experiment and the results obtained.

2. What answers do the data from this study provide for the research questions?

3. What conclusions can be drawn from this experiment about the influence of word-of-mouth communication in comparison with impersonal sources in bringing about product adoption?

Interview Guide

Directions: Ask the following questions in the order indicated, and record all responses as accurately as possible.

Opening Remarks: (Show credentials and identification.) "We are engaged in a study to learn something about the effectiveness of direct-mail advertising. All answers will be confidential, and the results will be reported as percentages and not by individuals."

1. Did you receive a letter and coupon offering a product for sale at a special price recently?

    Yes ____   No ____

2. Did you personally redeem the coupon?

    Yes ____   No ____

3. What date did you redeem the coupon?

4. Did you talk to anyone about the coupon offer? Who? (List names, and indicate whether they live in the housing unit or elsewhere.)

             Name   Where Live

Take each name listed in question 4, and secure answers to the following questions. (If the respondent indicates that he or she talked to no one, proceed to question 9.) Circle the best response.

5. Did (name) *contact you* or did you *contact her*/him?

6. Did the conversation occur *before* or *after* you purchased the product?

7. What aspects of the offer were discussed?

    Letter and Coupon

    Use of Product

    Other (write in)

8. Did you consider the comments as favorable or unfavorable to the product?

9. (Opinion Leader Question) When you want information about a product that you have not tried yet, who in this housing unit do you usually ask? Please list three people in order of priority, if possible.

10. Would you like to make some comments about the coupon offer?

Concluding Remarks: "We appreciate your willingness to answer these questions. They will contribute to our understanding of direct-mail advertising. Thank you for participating."

Experiment 10.2
Opinion Change and the Two-Step Flow

Proposition

Instigating change in large social systems requires the implementation of a series of clearly defined steps; the mass media may often produce the desirable changes by influencing opinion leaders through early exposure.

Research Questions

Does exposure to mediated communication alone induce changes in belief in opinion leaders?

Are nonleaders induced by exposure to mediated communication to seek advice about the message topic?

Do leaders and nonleaders alike who seek advice about a message topic after being exposed to mediated communication exhibit more changes of belief than persons who do not ask for advice?

Research Methods*

Subjects

A random sample of 100 persons who are already receiving a *bulletin* that is distributed regularly and that gives suggestions and urges people to adopt new ways of doing things. The bulletin may be one that is prepared and distributed by the Agricultural Extension Service, a garden club, a professional association such as dental hygienists, or a state automobile association. The sample population will receive an issue of the bulletin with 2 extra pages.

A control group of 30 individuals who are already recipients of the bulletin but who will receive the regular bulletin (minus the 2 extra pages).

An organization that agrees to your inserting 6 persuasive messages in an issue of their bulletin and to your interviewing the recipients prior to and after distribution of the bulletin.

Materials

Six persuasive messages presenting recommendations relevant to a new way of doing something with which recipients of the bulletin are concerned.

An Opinion Questionnaire (260 copies), and an Opinion Leadership Questionnaire (130 copies). (*Note:* A sample opinion questionnaire appears on page 275, but the researcher must structure his or her own questionnaire.)

Postbulletin Interview Guide (130 copies). (*Note:* A sample appears on page 277, but the researcher must structure his or her own guide.)

*Adapted from an experiment reported in Verling C. Troldahl, "A Field Test of a Modified 'Two-Step Flow of Communication' Model," *Public Opinion Quarterly*, Vol. 30 (1966–67), pp. 609–623). By permission.

Procedures

1. Selection of Subjects and Stimulus Materials
    a. Ask the editor of the bulletin if you may insert 6 persuasive messages for this experiment.
    b. In cooperation with the editor of the bulletin, select 6 topics on which persuasive messages can be written. (In a study similar to this one, the experimenter used horticultural beliefs. The persuasive messages concerned the advisability of cutting lawns 2 inches high, cutting lawns in the late fall, cleaning stalks from the garden in the fall, raking leaves from lawns in the fall, mulching perennial flowers after a hard freeze, and spraying weeds in the fall.)

2. Conduct of the Experiment
    a. Using the Preopinion Questionnaire, conduct a poll in person and then select 100 experimental subjects and 30 control subjects from 1 to 4 weeks prior to the publication of the special issue of the bulletin; in the poll, ascertain demographic data and their beliefs on the 6 message topics; also administer orally the Opinion Leadership Questionnaire.
    b. Either inserted in or attached to the next regular issue of the bulletin, the persuasive messages on 6 different relevant issues should be distributed to all but the sample of 30 control subjects.
    c. About 2 weeks following the date of mailing the bulletin, administer the Opinion Questionnaire in person to the sample of 100 experimental subjects and the 30 control subjects. Other questions as suggested in the Postbulletin Interview Guide can also be asked about face-to-face versus mediated communication and about bulletin readership.

3. Tabulation of the Data
    a. Tabulate the number of individuals designated as Opinion Leaders in both the experimental and control samples. Persons answering "yes" or "more likely" to either of the questions on the Opinion Leadership Questionnaire should be classified as Opinion Leaders.

	Exper. Group	Control Group
No. of Opinion Leaders		
Percentage of Opinion Leaders (divide total sample into the no. of O.L.'s)		

b. Tabulate the number of Opinion Leaders for each group who recalled one or more of the experimental persuasive messages.

Exper. Group	Control Group

c. Calculate the difference between the Opinion Leaders and the Nonleaders (in both groups) in terms of the percentage of each recalling the experimental messages.

Exper. Group	Control Group

d. Calculate the average change in opinion for each group from the Preopinion Questionnaire to the Postopinion Questionnaire. Use only subjects who reported reading the issue. Sum the scores of experimental Opinion Leaders, control Opinion Leaders, experimental Nonleaders, and control Nonleaders on the Preopinion Questionnaire and on the Postopinion Questionnaire for each of the 6 messages. Divide the sum by the number of subjects in each group. Tabulate the results as follows:

	Opinion Changes Induced by Persuasive Messages for Opinion Leaders and Nonleaders						
	Questionnaire Item Mean Change						
	1	2	3	4	5	6	(N)
Opinion Leaders Experimental Group							
Control Group							
Difference							
Nonleaders Experimental Group							
Control Group							
Difference							

e. Tabulate the number of respondents who reported that they had asked for advice.

Opinion Leaders	Nonleaders

f. Tabulate the number of Opinion Leaders and Nonleaders who had been sought for advice by someone else.

Opinion Leaders	Nonleaders

Name _____ Section _____

Date _____ Instructor _____

Results

1. What kinds of opinion changes occurred?

2. Were opinion leaders more persuaded than nonleaders?

3. From whom did opinion leaders and nonleaders seek advice? Is there a difference?

4. Was there a difference in attitude change between those who asked for advice and those who had been sought out for advice? Explain.

Explanation

1. Write a concise summary of this experiment and the results obtained.

2. How do the results of this study help answer the research questions?

3. What implications do the results of this study have for the effects of persuasive messages sent to people by means of bulletins of the type studied? How could more change of opinion be ensured?

Pre- and Postopinion Questionnaire (Sample)

(This questionnaire may be administered orally or by allowing respondent to mark responses on the form.)

Please indicate the degree to which you *agree* or *disagree* with each of the following statements:

1. (State recommendation 1 presented in the experimental issue of the bulletin.)

    Agree ___ : ___ : ___ : ___ : ___ : ___ : ___ Disagree
           1   2   3   4   5   6   7

2. (State recommendation 2 presented in the experimental issue of the bulletin.)

    Agree ___ : ___ : ___ : ___ : ___ : ___ : ___ Disagree
           1   2   3   4   5   6   7

3. (State recommendation 3 presented in the experimental issue of the bulletin.)

    Agree ___ : ___ : ___ : ___ : ___ : ___ : ___ Disagree
           1   2   3   4   5   6   7

4. (State recommendation 4 presented in the experimental issue of the bulletin.)

    Agree ___ : ___ : ___ : ___ : ___ : ___ : ___ Disagree
           1   2   3   4   5   6   7

5. (State recommendation 5 presented in the experimental issue of the bulletin.)

    Agree ___ : ___ : ___ : ___ : ___ : ___ : ___ Disagree
           1   2   3   4   5   6   7

6. (State recommendation 6 presented in the experimental issue of the bulletin.)

    Agree ___ : ___ : ___ : ___ : ___ : ___ : ___ Disagree
           1   2   3   4   5   6   7

Closing (Preopinion Questionnaire only)

Record the following items of demographic data for each respondent:

Name:

Age:

Sex:

Years of Education:

Occupation (and position):

Opinion Leadership Questionnaire (Sample)

(Administer this questionnaire orally.)

1. Has anyone you know *asked* you for your advice or opinion recently about (broad area of all message topics)?

2. Compared with *most* people you know, would you guess you're *more likely* or *less likely* to be asked to give opinions or advice about (broad area of all message topics)?

Postbulletin Interview Guide (Sample)

Directions: Ask the following questions in the order indicated, and record the most accurate answers possible.

Opening Remarks: "We are engaged in a readership study of the (bulletin name). The (editor's name) has approved this survey; here is a statement from (the editor) indicating his approval. Would you take a few moments to answer a few questions?"

1. Do you remember anything you read in the most recent issue of the (bulletin) concerning (the broad area of all message topics)? (Circle one.)

    Yes   No

Can you recall something specific? (Note which specific message topics the respondent refers to.)

2. Within the past week, have you asked for advice or information about any of the practices noted in the Opinion Questionnaire just completed? If so, which one?

3. From whom did you seek the advice? (Secure the person's name and professional position, if possible.)

4. How well would you estimate that you know the person from whom you sought advice? (Circle one.)

Very Well, Personal Friend	Casual Acquaintance on a Professional Basis	Not Well— Only by Title

5. Has anyone asked you for advice about any of the practices noted in the Opinion Questionnaire within the past week? (Circle one.)

    Yes   No

If so, which topic?

6. Who asked for advice? (Secure name and position.)

7. How well would you estimate that you know the person who sought your advice? (Circle one:)

    Very Well   Casual Acquaintance   Not Well

8. Do you read the (bulletin) regularly?

9. How well would you estimate you read the (bulletin)? (Circle one:)

   Entire Contents   Select Articles   Hardly at All

10. What do you like best about the (bulletin)?

11. How could it be improved?

Conclusion:
Beyond Research

Research can help us to know. To know means that we are able to explain, describe, and predict what will happen. Scientific knowledge consists of generalizations and specific statements about the past, but that kind of knowledge is useful in dealing with events in the future. By having some understanding of how people communicate and of the factors that influence the communication process, we may be able to predict somewhat accurately what will happen under a variety of circumstances and be able to adjust our everyday, practical communication behavior so that we can communicate more efficiently and more effectively.

The scholar-researcher, the communicologist, is interested in knowing. The user-practitioner, the communicator, is interested in doing. We contend that doing something depends on the accuracy of our knowledge. This is not to say that scholar-researchers do things best, nor does it say that user-practitioners always know why they do what they do. Too much "common sense" tells us that there are warm, lovable, efficient, effective communicators who know very little about the scientific data that explains how and why they communicate. Likewise, we are all too aware of the scholar who lacks the skill to communicate with him- or herself, much less with another person.

Practical knowledge is that which helps us to communicate better. If we want to accomplish a communication task, we should have available information that will help us complete the task in an efficient and effective manner. Nearly all the research described in this manual might be called *applied* research, in that it attempts to solve some rather clear and immediate practical problems concerning communication. The results of each of the experiments included in this manual could help someone to make his or her communication behavior easier, more efficient, or more effective.

Ours is not a "knowledge-for-its-own-sake" approach, but rather a "knowledge-for-what-it-can-do-for-us" approach. In the field of communication, this practical approach consists of translating what we know into specific skills, attitudes, and strategies. For years the main concern of large numbers of authors was to draft lists, brief descriptions, and long treatises on what they thought a person ought to do to "make friends" (establish effective relationships) and "influence people" (bring about change). Although too often overly simplistic, those practical suggestions certainly did help a lot of people. As a matter of fact, they continue to help people even today. Where those helpful hints are based on the available research in the field, they have the potential of being more useful. The more we know, the greater is the likelihood that we will offer few weak ideas and more good ideas.

Our charge, and the desire of most people, is for you to go beyond research. Seek to develop those skills and attitudes that will make you better communicators. Nevertheless, constantly ask the occasionally embarrassing questions, "How do we know that's the thing to do? What evidence do we have to justify that approach? What research do we have to support doing it that way?" Use the inquiring frame of mind to which you have been introduced in this manual. Take a scientific approach to communication in your everyday communication activities.

Now, a final admonition: Try not to make this your last course in communication. Develop your skills further by building on this foundation. Refine your writing skills by taking a course in composition. Expand your abilities in speechmaking by taking a course in public speaking. Enlarge your self-understanding by taking a course in interpersonal communication. Improve your abilities to interact in small groups by taking a course in discussion. Understand more about how bureaucracies influence our lives by taking a course in organizational communication. Explore your nonlanguage behavior by taking a course in nonverbal communication. Develop your personal face-to-face skills by taking a course in interviewing. Go beyond the research, and acquire the personal skills that will improve your day-to-day relationships.